EYE SIGNS

EYE SIGNS

**What your eyes reveal about
your health, emotions, personality
and love life**

———————

Adam J. Jackson

Thorsons
An Imprint of HarperCollins*Publishers*

Thorsons
An Imprint of HarperCollins*Publishers*
77–85 Fulham Palace Road
Hammersmith, London W6 8JB
1160 Battery Street
San Francisco, California 94111–1213

Published by Thorsons 1995

10 9 8 7 6 5 4 3 2 1

© Adam J. Jackson 1995

Illustrations by Chris Etheridge

Adam J. Jackson asserts the moral right to
be identified as the author of this work
A catalogue record for this book
is available from the British Library

ISBN 1 85538 419 1

Printed in Great Britain by
HarperCollins Manufacturing Glasgow

For my wife, Karen, and my daughter, Sophie
whose eyes light up every day of my life –
with love, always.

He speaketh not; and yet there lies
A conversation in his eyes.

Henry Wordsworth Longfellow

Contents

Acknowledgements

I would like to thank the following people who have freely spared their time and shared their knowledge and expertise with me during the research and preparation of this book: John Spector, Consultant Psychologist at Watford General Hospital; my good friend, Derek Spivack, Optometrist; Ronald Waldorf, Medical Physiologist and Chairman of EyeDynamics Inc; Kirit Patel, Optometrist; David Dhooma, Contact Lens Practitioner; Professor Peter Bedford of the Royal Veterinary College, and Robert Gardiner, Veterinary Surgeon.

I would also like to thank my literary agent, Sara Menguc, for her encouragement and advice from the very outset of the project, not to mention her efforts in finding the right publisher. My thanks also to Erica Smith at Thorsons for believing in and commissioning the book.

Last, but by no means least, I would like to thank my wife, Karen, my most candid editor and proof reader, for her continued enthusiasm, love and support throughout the writing of this book.

Introduction

Who would believe that so small a space could contain
the images of all the universe.
Leonardo da Vinci

Imagine meeting someone for the first time and, immediately, being able to see specific health problems such as anaemia (lack of iron), jaundice or high cholesterol levels. Imagine being able to see hypertension, nervous exhaustion or post-traumatic stress disorder. Imagine being able to read someone's thought processes and emotions, or tell if someone is being honest or dishonest, excited or bored. Imagine being able to know for certain whether someone is physically attracted to you . . . just from looking at their eyes!

Throughout the ages the eyes were believed by ancient sages and philosophers to be the windows of the soul; today they are acknowledged by health practitioners, scientists and psychologists to be mirrors of our bodies and minds revealing precise details about the state of our physical health, our emotions, our character traits, our personalities, and even our thoughts.

It sounds incredible, and indeed it is. When I first came across the subject of personal analysis through the eyes, I was amazed. How could something as small as the eyes reveal over 3,000 different conditions related to our health? How could our personality and character traits be hidden in our eyes? And, how could our eyes possibly reveal our emotions and thought processes?

The mystery of the eyes so intrigued and fascinated me

that I have spent much of the past eight years working in and researching the various sciences involving eye analysis from around the world. The deeper my research took me, the more exciting were my findings. Physicians diagnosing health problems; psychologists identifying specific emotions, thought processes and mental disorders; physiognomists uncovering character and personality traits, and today, trained law enforcement officers are able to evaluate drug and alcohol abuse in suspects ... through the eyes.

Every time you look at someone, you are in effect, looking into their body and mind ... the signs are in the eyes.

Adam J. Jackson
Hertfordshire
1994

CHAPTER I

The Eyes –
the Windows of the Soul

The light of the body is the eye.
Jesus (Matthew 6:,22)

At a provincial university in England, a group of male psychology students are shown two photographs of the same woman and asked which of the two is more attractive. Incredibly, all but a few of the men independently make the same choice. But why? The two photographs are virtually identical; it is the same woman, in the same pose, in the same surroundings.

The lecturer in charge of the experiment smiles. There is one small and very subtle difference between the photographs about which the students were not consciously aware, but the difference was so significant that virtually all of the men subconsciously responded to it. And that difference lay in the pupils of the woman's eyes.

The lecturer explains, to the amazement of the class, that this simple experiment has been done thousands of times in universities all over the world with the same results. It demonstrates that, in matters of sexual and physical attraction, the eyes play a prominent role.

In Mexico, a national survey of mothers conducted by the National Institute of Nutrition asks how they assess their children's well-being. What factors do they consider? As expected, the mothers' answers included their children's behavioural changes, facial complexion and body temperature. But the survey revealed that greater than these, and any disease symptoms, that mothers are most concerned about something else ... the appearance of their children's eyes.

Even when considering the worsening or improvement of diarrhoea (a common and potentially life-threatening illness in third world countries) whilst the mothers rely on obvious symptoms related to changes in the child's well-being ... *the more important signs that they recognize are focused on the child's eyes.*[1]

Back in England, a £4 million campaign to halt the creeping menace of drugs in schools is launched by the government. As part of that campaign, a sixty-page document is published containing detailed advice for teachers and parents on how to identify which children may be potential drug abusers and dealers, and how to handle those pupils who have overdosed.

The tell-tale signs of drug abuse, the report advises, include heavy use of scents or colognes to disguise the smell of drugs, lack of appetite, sores or rashes, especially around the mouth or nose, mood swings, irritability and temper tantrums. However, the most reliable and easily observed indication of drug abuse lies in the children's eyes. In fact, the sign – severely dilated or constricted pupils – is so easily recognizable that many children who take drugs can only hide the fact by wearing sunglasses.[2]

The Mystery of the Eyes

Why is it that the eyes, above all other facial features, reveal so much about a person?

What is so special about these two small organs which enables them to reflect the workings of our mind and body so exactly, so accurately?

The human eye is one of the great wonders of Nature. No larger than a ping-pong ball, it is by far the most complex

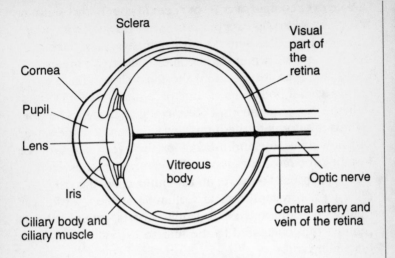

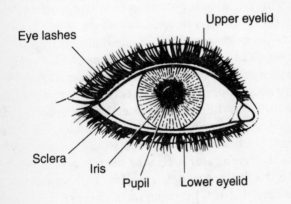

Figure 1.1:Anatomy of the human eye.
(a) cross-sectional view of the eyeball
(b) frontal view of the eye

and mysterious of all human organs. In fact, nothing on earth can compete with the incredible precision of your eyes, precision that relays over two billion messages to and from your brain every second!

3

Your eyes contain over 70 per cent of your body's sensory receptors. With the exception of blind people (who adapt and develop other senses) approximately 90 per cent of everything we learn in our lifetimes is learned through our eyes. Your eyes are therefore the most significant sensory organs in your body.

If you compare the most advanced man-made technological machinery with the human eye, it soon becomes clear just how awesome and miraculous the eyes really are. For instance, the most advanced video camera has thousands of photoreceptors. Your eye, on the other hand, has over 137 billion photoreceptors. The Columbia space shuttle was built with approximately 5.2 million parts, yet even this is pitiful when compared to the human eye which has over one billion parts.

In spite of all the technological advances of the twentieth century, scientists can still only marvel at the workings of the human eye. With tens of millions of electrical connections which have the capability of handling an estimated 1.5 million simultaneous messages, the eye is infinitely more intricate in design and function than any man-made device. If ever there was proof of divinity, it is the existence of the human eye. In fact, when Charles Darwin was asked 'How did the human eye evolve?' he answered that to even consider that the human eye evolved would be 'absurdity in the highest degree', and such was his reverence for the human eye, that in a passage from his correspondence, Darwin confessed that 'The thought of the eye made me cold all over.'[3]

The Eyes and the Soul

The soul, fortunately, has an interpreter – often an unconscious but still a faithful interpreter – in the eye.
Charlotte Brontë, *Jane Eyre*

All of the major world religions consider the eyes to be sacred. The eyes are believed to be much more than just visual apparatus; they contain images of the body, mind and spirit. The renowned spiritual leaders from western and eastern religions share the belief that the eyes are indeed reflections of the spirit. With the eyes we see the outside world, but through the eyes the outside world sees inside us, to the core of our soul.

This is perhaps why the eyes came to be known as the 'windows of the soul'. 'Dim windows of the soul,' wrote William Blake, 'eyes tell much about the human spirit.' Beyond feelings, beyond emotions and mental processes, the eyes are seen as a reflection of a man's soul, revealing his spiritual nature. Jesus himself said: 'The light of the body is the eye; therefore when thine eye is clear, thy whole body is clear, thy whole body is also full of light; but when it is unclear, your body is full of darkness.'[4] Confucius, it would seem, was also aware of the significance of the eyes in relation to a man's psyche. He said: 'Look into a man's pupils. He cannot hide himself.'

In Judaism, the eyes are considered to be closely related to the heart and mind. Like Christianity, the eyes are believed to reflect our innermost being. Indeed, the special respect in Judaism for the human eye is evidenced by the fact that it is the only organ which, if injured on a sabbath day, allows the sabbath rules to be broken so that treatment may be sought. No other injury – which is not life threatening – to any other part of the body permits the Sabbath laws to be violated.

The Eyes, the Brain and the Nervous System

Biology shows us that the eye is a part of the brain, the place, if you like, where the brain rises to the surface.
Montague Ruben, consultant ophthalmologist and author

Medical science confirms the theologists' contention that our eyes are far more than just divinely manufactured video cameras; they are, quite literally, extensions of the brain. In fact, when you were just a foetus, your eyes were part of your brain. It was only as you developed in your mother's

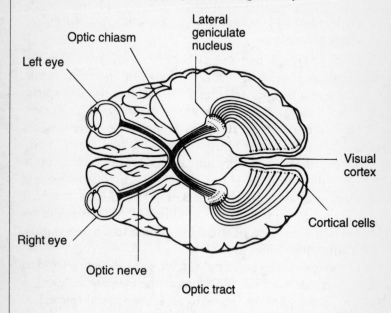

Figure 1.2:The eye-brain connection.

womb that your eyes separated from the brain, but they remained connected via the optic nerve.

It is this intimate relationship between the eyes and the brain that explains, in part, how the eyes are able to reveal so much about our physical health and emotional states. Your brain monitors every thought in your mind and controls every function in your body and because the eyes are connected to the brain, everything is recorded in them.

For the past century, the eyes have been examined to diagnose diseases of the central nervous system.[5] According to Ronald Waldorf, a medical physiologist and specialist in the field of vestibular (balance) disorders, who has served as principal investigator on numerous private and US Government sponsored research programmes over a period of 20 years, the eyes provide 'the cornerstone for the diagnostic tests associated with vertigo, imbalance, and the more diffuse feelings of lightheadedness.'

Mr Waldorf, as chairman of Eyedynamics Inc. – a public company dedicated to advancing the use of technology for eye-related functions – headed the research team that produced portable, infrared video equipment with the capability to monitor the eyes so precisely that it can accurately assess not only neurological and vestibular disorders, but it can also evaluate drug and alcohol intoxication.[6] The machine (marketed as the EM/1 Eye Observation system) has numerous applications aside from being a safe, quick, non-invasive and extremely accurate diagnostic tool for use in medicine. For instance, the EM/1 is proving to be a cost-saving tool in numerous areas of law enforcement; it is used by trained road traffic police officers to test the condition of a driver suspected of driving under the influence of alcohol or drugs. The EM/1 is also used by probation and parole officers to monitor the habits of the people under their care.

The test takes less than 90 seconds to complete and, in a world where drug and alcohol abuse has reached epidemic proportions, the EM/1, using a simple analysis of a person's eyes, can be used at schools, in the workplace and in sporting arenas to help identify and eliminate drug or alcohol abuse.

Dr Louis H. Schwartz, an eye specialist and lecturer in Ophthalmology, who has been the attending ophthalmologist at the Harlem Eye and Ear Hospital in New York, has no doubts that the human eye is an accurate barometer of our physical and mental health. He writes:

A study of the eyes will many times elicit data which cannot be found elsewhere. From an examination of the eyes, the ophthalmologist is often able to tell much more than the patient's state of health at the moment; he may bring to light maladies from which the patient has long since recovered, and he may even venture to predict, with uncanny certainty, disorders which will ensue in the months or years ahead.[7]

The Eyes and Nutrition

No physical check-up is complete without a careful examination of the eyes.
Dr Louis H. Schwartz MD

The importance of the eyes in relation to our general health is reflected in the nutritional demands they make on the body. For example, whilst the eyes are but a minute fraction of our total body weight, together with the brain they require approximately one quarter of our nutritional intake. The eyes alone need more zinc than any other organ in the body, they use one third as much oxygen as the heart, and they require twenty times more vitamin C as our joint capsules.

It is therefore little wonder that nutritional deficiencies (e.g. anaemia (lack of iron), calcium deficiencies and poor copper metabolism) as well as many systemic health problems (e.g. hardening of the arteries, goitre and jaundice) are often first diagnosed in the eyes *(see Chapter 3)*.

Eye Diseases and Disorders

The origin of eye diseases is the general bodily condition of the individual sufferer, and his past medical history.
Harry Benjamin, *Better Sight Without Glasses*

At the turn of this century, a medical 'heretic' taught that most eye diseases and disorders were nothing more than symptoms, the causes of which lay elsewhere in the body. According to Dr W. H. Bates, a pioneer of natural eye care and visual education, nutritional deficiencies, emotional strain and physical stress were responsible for many eye problems.

For instance, it was Dr Bates' contention that cataract – a condition in which the crystalline lens in the eye becomes clouded and can lead to blindness – was simply a symptom of an impure bloodstream caused by poor nutrition. Consequently, Dr Bates recommended a cleansing diet with plenty of fresh fruits and vegetables as an essential part of the treatment and prevention of cataract.

Although the good doctor was ridiculed by his peers, medical research in the past five years has vindicated his theories. Researchers all over the world have arrived at the same conclusion – the most important factor affecting the two greatest causes of blindness throughout the world – cataract and glaucoma – is nutrition.[8] Even the World Health Organization has stated that the problem of cataract could be halved through improved hygiene and adequate nutrition.[9] This means that of the 50 million people who suffer with cataract every year, at least 25 million, a number almost equal to the entire population of Canada, could effectively prevent the onset of the disease through simple nutritional measures ensuring adequate intake of the anti-oxidant nutrients – vitamins A, C and E.

Eye Diseases, Mental Health and Personality Disorders

Most of us are not aware that eyesight is merely a small aspect of that dynamic process known as vision. We are much less aware that our eyes, as major access routes by which light enters the body, can be mirrors of our general and emotional health as well as accurate indicators of our styles of thinking and learning.
Professor Jacob Liberman OD, PhD

Scientists have also found that there is a significant relationship between chronic eye diseases and disorders (e.g. glaucoma, keratoconus) and mental illness. For instance, it has been estimated that only nine per cent of the general population suffer with chronic eye diseases or disorders, yet approximately 66 per cent of those people suffering from depression, schizophrenia or alcoholism have chronic eye disorders.[10]

Medical studies have found that patients with chronic eye diseases tend to be paranoid, hypomanic and less conforming with strong tendencies to extreme aggression or docility. The patients with eye diseases were also observed to have highly disorganized thought patterns as well as a significantly higher incidence of drug abuse and alcoholism when compared to the general population.[11]

Slowly, but surely, medical evidence is revealing that many eye disorders are, as Dr Bates contended 80 years ago, simply reflections of deeper physical and psychological health problems.

The Eyes and Communication

It is through the eyes that we attain the most intimate communion with other human beings.
John Brophy, physiognomist and author

Cover up the eyes on a photograph and you cover up the person. This is why so many famous people choose to wear sunglasses. They can hide behind them, never revealing their true feelings, never really communicating.

All psychologists agree that, with the exception of the mother–child relationship (which first bonds through touch), all communication begins with eye contact. The eyes reveal friendliness or animosity, interest or apathy, attraction or revulsion. In fact, the eyes in many ways tell you more about what a person is feeling than what he says.

Words can be contrived, the tongue may deceive, but the subconscious language of the eyes never lies.

The reason why the eyes are so expressive and communicative is because they are controlled by the same portion of the brain that monitors and controls our feelings and emotions – the limbic system. This is why all feelings and emotions cause subconscious involuntary reactions in our eyes and the way we use them.

In his book, *The Tell-Tale Eye*, Dr Eckhard Hess, a psychologist at the University of Chicago explains that the eyes are the most revealing and accurate of all human communication signals because they are the focal point on the body and are controlled, in many ways, by our subconscious.[12] In fact, Dr Hess found that the eyes accurately express our emotional responses to virtually anything experienced including sounds, odours, tastes and the human voice. Researchers at Linkoping University, Sweden,[13] recently demonstrated that Hess was right. In a controlled clinical study the researchers established that the eyes are the most important non-verbal communication which, along with a smile, accounts for more than 50 per cent of total communication, especially in the greeting situation.

Amazing as it sounds, the researchers found that we communicate with our eyes more than our mouths in a face-to-face social situation. Such is the power of the messages relayed through the eyes that even patients undergoing psychotherapy – people who by the nature of their illness experience difficulty in communication – were keenly aware of the messages relayed through the movement, and gaze, of a person's eyes.

The Eyes in Nature

To this day the eye makes me shudder.
Charles Darwin

Throughout the animal kingdom, there remains a world of untold mysteries related to the eyes of animals, birds and reptiles. For instance, the chameleon is renowned for its ability to change the colour of its skin to camouflage itself within its environment and so protect itself from predators, but its ability to do this is directly related to its eyes. In fact, if one eye of a chameleon is covered up, the corresponding side of its body will not change colour, and if it loses its sight, its skin will immediately turn a dull, grey colour and remain that way for the rest of its life.[14] Without its eyes, the chameleon loses its ability to change the colour of its skin.

The chameleon is not the only creature which can change the colour of its skin; the octopus, the mysis (a species of shrimp) and many fish exhibit the same phenomenon. Toward the end of the nineteenth century, Pouchet, the renowned French scientist, discovered that certain fish – carp, stickleback, roach and perch – all turn a bright colour when kept in an uncovered china vessel, but as soon as the vessel is covered, their scales turn darker. Further investigations revealed that blinded fish turned a dull, dark colour and were no longer affected by different environments. More remarkably, those fish which were blind in one eye turned and remained a dull, dark colour on the corresponding side of its body, but the side of the body corresponding with the good eye continued to change colour in response to different environments.

Some mammals also show a strong relationship between their eyes and their skin. The winter hare in Scandinavia, for instance, is known for its ability to change the colour of its fur from brown to white in the winter, taking on the colour of the snow. Dr H. Anderschou, author of *Iris Science*[15] reported an incident in which he personally saw the body of a winter hare that had been shot and, to his amazement, the right side of the hare's body was white and the left side was a greyish brown. Dr Anderschou reported:

On closer examination it turned out that the animal had lost its left eye, which had presumably been destroyed a considerable time before, and now in the winter only the right side, through the expression of reflection from the eyes, had changed its colour in correspondence with the colour of the snow, and as the left eye was lost, the left side of the body did not change.[16]

Without the use of its eye, the winter hare was unable to effectively camouflage itself and this had made it easy prey for the hunters.

The eyes of pigeons have also been shown to be particularly significant in assessing the bird's health. For hundreds of years, pigeon breeders have relied upon what they see in the pigeons' eyes to help them select good racing pigeons. In Fulton's *Book of Pigeons* first published in 1895, the author notes:

Round the iris is sometimes found a circle or line of darkish blue, and as a rule such birds, being good in other respects, are highly esteemed.[17]

Many pigeon breeders are now able to establish whether a bird has champion qualities just by looking at the bird's eyes. Studying over 53,000 pigeons, Mr S.W. Bishop, pigeon breeder and author of *The Secret of Eye Sign*, found that there were indeed distinct differences between the markings in the eyes of birds that were champion racers and those that were not, and he was able to grade pigeons' racing and fitness form, just by examining their eyes.

The work of veterinary surgeons and zoologists has also confirmed that the eyes have special significance throughout the animal kingdom. Many of the health problems affecting humans that are diagnosed in the eyes are also evident in animals' eyes. Diabetes, anaemia, jaundice, high blood pressure and thyroid disorders, along with a myriad of other health problems, can all be diagnosed, in the first instance, through the animals' eyes. This is why veterinary surgeons closely examine their patients' eyes as part of a routine check-up.

The markings in the eyes of animals are especially important because animals cannot tell us when they are in pain. Professor Peter Bedford, of the Royal Veterinary College in England, told me that all too often domestic animals are taken to a vet only *after* disease symptoms have progressed to an advanced stage. Like many human diseases, some of those affecting animals can take nine years or more to develop into clinical symptoms and many of these can be diagnosed in their early stages through the eyes. 'This is why it is absolutely essential,' explained Professor Bedford, 'and should be compulsory, for all pedigrees to be checked by a vet annually because one animal can perpetuate a genetic disease in hundreds of offspring. Some diseases can pass undetected in pups and kittens for several years.'

It is for this reason that Professor Bedford advises owners of domestic animals to always be aware of minor changes in their animals' eyes and ensure that they take their animals to a vet at least once a year for a full health check-up. The eyelids should appear normal, the cornea transparent, the sclera white-pink in colour and the pupil should be clear and react to variations in light. Any abnormal markings should be immediately referred to a veterinary surgeon.

Discovering the secrets

We can therefore begin to see how science is now confirming the wisdom in the ancient belief that the eyes are the windows of the soul. We can only now begin to understand the greater meanings behind the words of the prophet: 'The light of the body is the eye.'

Researchers are beginning to understand the strong re-lationships that exist between our eyes, our bodies and our minds. With the little that we now know, we can begin to appreciate the significance of our eyes and how they are able to reveal secrets about our physical and mental health, our emotions, and even our thought processes. The windows of the soul are being opened, the secrets revealed . . .

Endnotes

1. Martinez, H., Saucedo, G., 'Mothers' perceptions about childhood diarrhoea in rural Mexico', Instituto Nacional de la Nutricion, Salvador Zubiran, Mexico DF, *Journal Diarrhoeal Disease Research* (Bangladesh) Sept 1991, 9 (3) pp.235-43.
2. Reported in the *Daily Mail*, 9 November 1994.
3. Ruben, M., Wintle, J., *Your Eyes and their Care*, Granada Publishing, 1985.
4. The Holy Bible – Luke 11:34 and Matthew 6:22.
5. Borries, GVTh, 'Vestibular Nystatgmus in the Nineteenth Century: Historical Study' *Acta Otolaryngol* 3 1922, pp.348-55.
6. Burns, M., 'Field of Sobriety Tests: An important component of DUI enforcement' *Alcohol, Drugs and Driving* 1 (3) 1985, pp.21-5.
7. 'The Eye as an Index of Health' published in *Iridology: The Science and Practice in the Healing Arts* by Dr B. Jensen, B. Jensen Publishing, 1952.
8. Schoenfeld, E.R., Leske, M. C., Wu S. Y., Recent epidemiologic studies on nutrition and cataract in India, Italy and the United States. Department of Preventive Medicine, SUNY at Stony Brook School of Medicine 11794-8036. *Journal of the American College of Nutrition* (US) Oct 1993, 12 (5), pp.521-6.
9. Taylor, A., 'Cataract: relationship between nutrition and oxidation' Laboratory for Nutrition and Vision Research, USDA Human Nutrition Research Center on Aging, Tufts University, Boston, MA 02111, *Journal of the American College of Nutrition* (US) Apr 1993, 12 (2) pp.138-46.
10. Arseneault, R. J., 'Blindness in the world: nursing experience in Nepal', *Journal of Ophthalmic Nursing Technology* (US) Nov-Dec 1992, 11 (6) pp.241-6.
11. Liberman, J., OD, PhD, *Light: Medicine of the Future* p.18, Bear & Co, 1991.

12. Mannis, M. J., Morrison, T. L., Zadnik, K., Holland, E. J., Krachmer, J. H., 'Personality trends in keratoconus. An analysis', *Archives of Opthalmology* (US) Jun 1987, 105 (6), pp.798–800.

13. Van Nostrand Reinhold 1975.

14. Astrom, J., Thorell, L. H., d'Elia, G., 'Attitudes towards and observations of nonverbal communication in a psychotherapeutic greeting situation: III. An interview study of outpatients' Linkoping University, Sweden. *Psychological Reports* (US) Aug 1993, 73 (1), pp.151–68.

15. Reported by Dr H. W. Anderschou in *Iris Science: Diagnosis of Bodily Diseases through Examination of the Eye,* Dr H. W. Anderschou, 1916.

16. Ibid pp.15–16.

17. Ibid p.16.

18. Reported by S. W. Bishop in *The Secret of Eye Sign*, p.429, S & D Bishop Ltd, 1988.

CHAPTER 2

The History of Eye Analysis

It was always the eyes, more than any other facial feature, that
particularly fascinated ancient writers.
John Liggett, former senior lecturer in Psychology, University of
Wales, *The Human Face*, Constable & Co, 1974

The assertion that the mind and body are reflected in the
eyes is by no means a new concept. For literally thousands of years, physicians, healers, philosophers, teachers
and spiritual leaders from all over the world have written
about, and spoken of, the different ways in which the
eyes reveal our health, emotions, character, personality
and thought processes. In fact, the list of renowned and
respected philosophers and physicians, both past and
present, who have acknowledged the significance of the
eyes in health diagnosis and personal analysis includes such
great names as Confucius, Hippocrates, Jesus, Pythagoras,
Aristotle, Galen, Adamantius and Meletius, Cicero, Ovid,
Paracelcus, Leonardo da Vinci, William Blake, Ralph Waldo
Emerson, and Henry Wordsworth Longfellow.

Hippocrates, the renowned 'Father of Medicine', would
always refer to his patients' eyes when forming a diagnosis.
One of his best-known observations was the 'Facies
Hippocratia' – the face of one about to die – in which the
most notable characteristics were sunken temples and dark,
hollow eyes. Today, medical science acknowledges that when
the eyes become heavily sunken and hollow, the fatty tissues
have wasted, indicating a serious degenerative disease.

Jesus said that the eyes revealed the very nature of a man's soul. To him, the eye was '*The* light of the body',[1] a reflection of the state of the whole of the body. Ancient Chinese physicians and soothsayers also placed great emphasis on the appearance of the eyes in both health diagnosis and personal analysis. Indeed, such is the significance of the eyes in the Orient that Confucius told his followers to always look into a person's eyes because there 'he cannot hide himself'.

In Ancient Greece, as far back as 500 BC, Pythagoras would look at the eyes of prospective students to 'see' if they were of sufficient intellect. It is reported that he would often not allow students to study at his prestigious academy if, in his judgement – based upon the appearance of a student's eyes – the student could not profit sufficiently from his teachings.[2]

Aristotle was also noted for his keen observations on the eyes, particularly in understanding one's character and personality. For instance, he concluded that straight eyebrows indicated a soft nature, whereas staring eyes revealed impudence.

Avicenna, the noted Arab philosopher and physician, wrote about the eyes, not only in health diagnosis but also in character analysis. He would, for instance, say that thick bushy eyebrows indicated guile and craftiness – a conclusion which we shall see later was also drawn by the orientals.

In the second century, the Greek physician Galen attached importance to the eyes when diagnosing his patients and, by the fourth century, the science of diagnosis through facial features had become an honoured and much sought-after profession in Greece.

European medical doctors and clinical psychologists have all used the eyes for personal analysis as far back as the seventeenth and eighteenth centuries. In 1670 a Polish physician called Philipus Meyens wrote *Chiromatic Medica*, referring to diagnosis through markings in the eye and, in 1735, Keogh Murphy, a Scottish physician wrote *Practitioner Medical Treatments*, in which he clearly cites the relationship of the appearance of his patients' eyes to their physical health.

Other peoples and sects including the Brahmins, the Jesuit priests, Tibetan Monks, and North American Indians all respected the relationship between a man's eyes and his health and emotions. Today, there are a number of recognized sciences which reveal how the eyes, their appearance, function and movement accurately reflect not only our physical health, but also our innermost thoughts and emotions.

Physiognomy (facial diagnosis)

Physiognomy is the analysis of facial features and characteristics to diagnose our physical health as well as assess our mental health, intellect and personality. It is perhaps one of the lesser-known sciences, yet it is one that has its roots in virtually every system of medicine.

It is inconceivable to think that a doctor would not, as part of his general diagnosis of a patient, consider the appearance and features of the patient's face. For instance, a pale complexion and hair loss are often indications of anaemia. A grey pallor is a sign of serious illness, cracked lips can be the result of a lack of vitamin B and a bulbous red nose is often the result of excess alcohol.

In Europe, the science of physiognomy developed alongside medicine. Physicians often noticed the change in their patients' facial appearances during the course of certain diseases as well as when the patients were recovering and from this they were able to develop the science of facial diagnosis. However, it was the observers of life, the scientists and philosophers (e.g. Pythagoras, Aristotle, Cicero, Avicenna and Lavater) who were most responsible for the development of character and personality analysis from the face.

19

In China, the science of physiognomy is known as 'Siang Mien'. Although it dates back to 4,000 years BC, to the *Nei Te Ching* (the oldest book of Oriental medicine), it continues to this day to be a much-respected and frequently-practised science in China. In fact, a number of the conclusions of this ancient science have in more recent years been acknowledged and adopted by conventional, Western medicine. For instance, bulging, protruding eyes were considered in Chinese medicine to be an indicator of a troubled thyroid gland. Today, it is well-accepted that the first and most prominent symptom of exophthalmic goitre (a disease of the thyroid gland in which it becomes enlarged and overactive) is indeed bulging and protruding eyes.

In Chinese medicine, our facial characteristics reveal the state of our general health and well-being but, according to the masters of Siang Mien, the face records our emotions, personality and character traits (see chapters 5 and 6). The accuracy of Siang Mien in assessing personality and character is testified by the fact that many practitioners of Siang Mien are now working in Western countries and their services are regularly employed by large corporations wishing to vet potential employees.

Yet, of all the facial features, the one which both European and Chinese physiognomists agree bears the most significance and tells us most about our health and emotions is ... the eyes. Whilst physiognomists consider all of the characteristics of the face (including the ears, the hairline, the mouth, nose and chin) when analysing a person, it is the eyes upon which they place the greatest emphasis. Everything is considered secondary to the significance of the markings in and around the eyes.

Iridology

Iridology is the science of health and personality analysis through the coloured portion of the eye known as the iris.

The irises are likened to miniature television screens, recording the condition of the organs and tissues through-out the body; bronchial congestion, hyper-acidity in the stomach, hardening of the arteries and an under-functioning immune system are just a few of the thousands of conditions that can be identified from the irises.

Iridology is by no means a new science; the eyes have been used by physicians and sages to diagnose a person's health for literally thousands of years. But iridology did not develop as a clinical science until the nineteenth century.

It was a Hungarian doctor and homoeopath called Ignatz von Peczely who first noticed the relationship between the iris of the eye and the rest of the body.

I was only eleven years old, when one day I tried to catch an owl that defended itself violently, and plunged its claws into my hand, and the more I tried to free my hand the deeper did the owl, with its claws pierce my flesh. There was no other way but to try by force to break the leg of the owl in order to extract the claw, and as I was a strong boy I succeeded in doing so.

During the struggle I and the owl chanced to look each other sharply into the eyes, and the very moment I broke the leg in two, I observed to my surprise a black streak appearing in one eye of the owl. However, a friend of animals, I took the bird home, bandaged its leg, and treated it until it again was well during which time the bird became so tame that it returned and ate at my table in the garden, and continued doing this a long time after it was liberated.

In the fall of the year the owl flew away, but next summer it returned and was quite tame as it had been the previous year. And one day sitting with it on my hand, I happened to notice the black streak in the one eye of the bird, and saw that it was there just as plainly as on the day when it originated, but it was now bordered and surrounded by white lines![3]

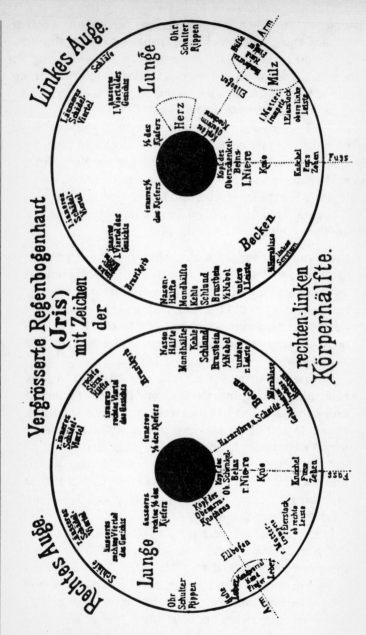

Figure 2.1: Iridology chart developed by Dr Ignatz von Peczely

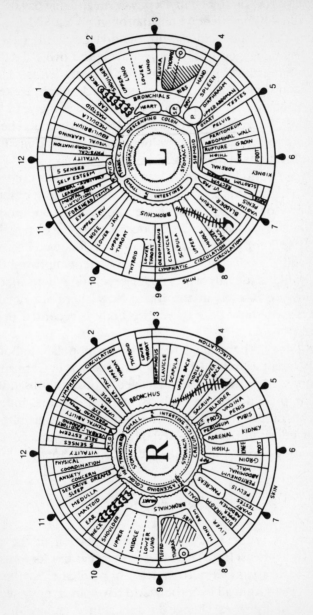

Figure 2.2: Iridology chart (© Adam J. Jackson)

Peczely grew up to become a physician and one day he was consulted by a patient who had broken his leg. Suddenly, he remembered the incident with the owl. Could the patient's eye have changed in the same way as the owl's? Taking a magnifying glass, he peered into the patient's left iris and to his astonishment, there was indeed a black streak. Excitedly, he examined all of his patients' eyes and, over the years that followed, Peczely observed that patients with similar health problems shared similar discolourations and markings in the same locations in their irises.

Over a period of years he was able to develop a crude iris chart *(see Figure 2.1)* which demonstrated how different sections of the iris actually recorded the condition of different organs and tissues inside the body.

Other European and American doctors followed Peczely's lead and, as optical photographic equipment improved, they were able to identify with greater precision where specific organs are located in the irises. Now there are detailed charts that show how the entire body is recorded in the irises.

Iridology is becoming an increasingly popular method of health analysis in the UK and North America. In Germany, it is very well-respected and practised by many thousands of health practitioners as well as medical doctors. Indeed, several of the lecturers at the International Institute of Irisdiagnosis in Germany – the oldest teaching college of its kind anywhere in the world – are medical doctors.

Sclerology

Sclerology is the study of the white portion of the eye known as the 'sclera'. This is a science that has its roots in both Eastern and Western systems of medicine. Physicians and healers from all over the world have observed how the whites of the eyes change in appearance and colour in response to specific physical diseases and dietary practices.

Blood vessels in: indicate problems with:

12–1	Head
1–2	Eyes, sinuses, nose
2–3	Mouth, throat, thyroid
3–4	Upper back
4–5	Lower back
5–6	Kidney, adrenal, bladder, prostate, uterus
6–7	Lower abdomen
7–8	Upper abdomen
8–9	Chest, breast
9–10	Lung
10–11	Neck, ear
11–12	Head

Blood vessels in: indicate problems with:

12–1	Head
1–2	Neck, ear
2–3	Lung
3–4	Chest, breast
4–5	Upper abdomen
5–6	Lower abdomen
6–7	Kidney, adrenal, bladder, prostate, uterus
7–8	Lower back
8–9	Upper back
9–10	Mouth, throat, thyroid
10–11	Eyes, sinuses, nose
11–12	Head

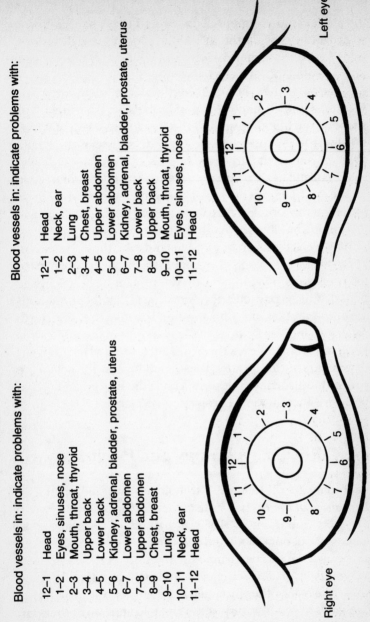

Right eye

Left eye

Figure 2.3: Sclerology chart – identifying health problems in the whites of the eyes.

Indeed it is now commonly accepted that changes in the sclera often provide the initial and most visible diagnostic signs for excess serum cholesterol, brittle bone disease, jaundice and alcoholism (see chapter 3).

Some branches of sclerology involve identifying the nature of the distinctive blood vessels in the sclera. The shape of the blood vessel and the area in the sclera in which it is located is thought to indicate the nature of the health problem and what part of the body is affected. According to some holistic health practitioners, the sclera contains a map of the body organs in much the same way as the iris in iridology, the foot in reflexology, the ear in acupuncture and the tongue in Indian ayurvedic medicine.

Whilst scientists do not understand why these systems of analysis should work, they have traditionally been used for thousands of years and therefore cannot be dismissed lightly. What is particularly interesting is that these methods seem to complement one another. For instance, the North American Indians found specific markings in the whites of a pregnant woman's eyes that revealed if she was having a girl or a boy *(see Chapter 8)*. These markings in the sclera are precisely adjacent to the positions of the ovaries and uterus in the iris identified by European physicians.

Clinical Psychology and Psychiatry

According to the clinical psychologist and author of *The Language of the Body*[4] Dr Alexander Lowen MD, the eyes are the most important of all facial features in revealing information about our moods and emotions, character and personality traits. 'We can determine the intensity of the expression as well as its quality. Some eyes are bright and sparkle, some shine like stars, others are dull and many are vacant . . . some eyes are sad, others angry; some are cold and hard, others are soft and appealing . . . If one is unaware of these things,' writes Dr Lowen, 'psychiatry becomes a lifeless profession.'[5]

Yet it is only in the last hundred years or so that psychologists and psychiatrists have begun to appreciate how our eyes are the external reflections of our emotions, our thought processes and the way we communicate. Scientists have been able to confirm, for instance, that the pupil of the eye can reveal our likes and dislikes, as well as feelings of excitement, stress, pain and physical attraction.

Scientists were also intrigued to find that patients suffering from a mental illness had a much higher incidence of chronic eye diseases – five times more, in fact – than the general public.[6] Researchers were able to prove that there is a definite link between mental health and eye health which is so strong that they recommended that neuro-ophthalmologists should collaborate and work alongside psychiatrists to establish the most appropriate remedial programmes for each patient. Such collaboration, it was said, would serve to further our understanding of the biological basis of psychiatry.[7]

As a result of the overwhelming clinical research linking the eyes with mental states and psychiatric disorders, psychologists turned their attention to their patients' eyes. They closely analysed the general appearance and movements of their patients' eyes, monitoring such things as the colours of the iris, pupil variations, the direction and frequency of the gaze, and the speed and manner in which the eyes moved and the eyelids blinked.

The results of much of their work were quite literally astounding; the researchers discovered that the movement and appearance of the eyes were indeed linked with our psyche and they were able to demonstrate through their experiments that the eyes are very reliable indicators of mental stability or illness. For instance, it is now well known that patients suffering with keratoconus (a disease affecting the cornea) and keratitis (inflammation of the cornea) are frequently described as having peculiar personality characteristics.[8] The worse the eye disease becomes, the greater the psychological abnormalities.

There is now overwhelming scientific data proving that our eyes are affected by our thought processes. There are numerous published scientific studies, undertaken by reputable scientists, which provide irrefutable evidence that our eyes are influenced by numerous mental illnesses including anxiety, schizophrenia and alexithymia.[9]

One of the major breakthroughs of this century in clinical psychology was the discovery that our eye movements can influence – as well as be influenced by – our emotions and thought processes. The result of this finding was that mental health problems could not only be diagnosed in the eyes, but that they could also be treated through the eyes. This discovery led to a revolutionary mode of treatment of many forms of mental illness including post-traumatic stress disorder, phobias and depression. A simple, non-invasive technique involving the conscious control of our eye movements has produced astounding results, wiping away chronic mental disorders that had persisted, despite years of drug therapy, in one session. This new method of treatment (known as Eye Movement Desensitization and Reprocessing (EMDR) is reported to be the quickest, safest and most effective mode of treatment for post-traumatic stress disorders ever known *(see Chapter 4)*.

Neuro-Linguistic Programming (NLP)

Neuro-linguistic programming (NLP) is a relatively new science which looks at the way we store information and process our thoughts, and how this affects our actions. It is a remarkable science which explains how, with an understanding of our behavioural mechanisms, we can control our mental and physical states and, in so doing, create our own destinies.

During the past decade, NLP has received considerable acclaim and gained widespread popularity, particularly in North America. This revolutionary new science was originally based upon clinical observations which demonstrated that the way we move our eyes is related to the way our brains process, store and access information. The researchers observed that people tend to move their eyes in specific directions when completing specific mental tasks *(see Chapter 7)*. For instance, over 90 per cent of right-handed people will move their eyes up and to the left when *remembering* a visual image but they will move their eyes up and to the right when *mentally constructing* a visual image.[10] Right-handed people will also tend to look sideways to the left when *remembering* a sound (e.g. a song or a statement) but they will look sideways to the right when *creating* sounds from their imagination. (The positions are precisely reversed for left-handed people.)

The researchers also discovered that the way we move our eyes during a conversation is linked not only to what we are thinking but it reveals a lot about our self-esteem, interest and boredom, honesty and deceit *(see Chapters 5 and 7)*.

As you can imagine, these eye-related sciences offer considerable benefits in our day-to-day lives. Through them, doctors are better able to accurately diagnose a patient's health, psychologists are provided with an accurate and objective mode of assessment of their patients' mental states, employers are able to improve their interview techniques of potential employees, educators can learn to communicate more effectively, and all of us can learn more about ourselves and each other.

Endnotes

1. Luke 11:34.
2. Reported by Terry Landau in *About Faces*, Doubleday, 1989.
3. Dr H. W. Anderschou in *Iris Science: Diagnosis of Bodily Diseases through Examination of the Eye,* Dr H. W. Anderschou, 1916.

4. Collier MacMillan Publishers, 1958.

5. p.106.

6. Liberman, J., OD, PhD, *Light: Medicine of the Future*, Bear & Co, 1991 p.18.

7. Newman, N. J., 'Neuro-ophthalmology and psychiatry', Neuro-Ophthalmology Unit, Emory Eye Center, Atlanta, GA 30322, *General Hospital Psychiatry* (US) Mar 1993, 15 (2), pp.102–14.

8. Swartz, N. G., Cohen, E. J., Scott, D. G., Genvert, G. I., Arentsen, J. J., Laibson, P. R., 'Personality and keratoconus', Cornea Service, Wills Eye Hospital, Philadelphia, PA 19107. *CLAO J* (US) Jan–Mar 1990, 16 (1), pp.62–4.

9. Lund, H. G., Bech, P., Eplov, L., Jennum, P., Wildschiodtz, G., 'An epidemiological study of REM latency and psychiatric disorders', Department of Psychiatry, Rigshospitalet, Copenhagen, Denmark, *Journal of Affective Disorders* (Netherlands) Nov 1991, 23 (3), pp.107–12.

10. Lencz, T., Raine, A., Scerbo, A., Redmon, M., Brodish, S., Holt, L., Bird, L., 'Impaired eye tracking in undergraduates with schizotypal personality disorder', Department of Psychology, University of Southern California, Los Angeles 90089–1061, *American Journal of Psychiatry* (US) Jan 1993, 150 (1), pp.152–4.

11. Siever, L. J., Keefe, R., Bernstein, D. P., Coccaro, E. F., Klar, H. M., Zemishlany, Z., Peterson, A. E., Davidson, M., Mahon, T., Horvath, T., et al, 'Eye tracking impairment in clinically identified patients with schizotypal personality disorder' Department of Psychiatry, Mount Sinai School of Medicine, Bronx, NY. *American Journal of Psychiatry* (US) Jun 1990, 147 (6), pp.740–5.

12. Parker, J. D., Taylor, G. J., Bagby, R. M., 'Relationship between conjugate lateral eye movements and alexithymia' Department of Psychology, York University, Toronto, Canada. *Psychotherapy & Psychosomatics* (Switzerland) 1992, 57 (3), pp.94–101.

13. Robbins, A., *Unlimited Power*, pp. 122–7, Simon & Schuster, 1986.

CHAPTER 3

Health in the Eyes

In ancient cultures the eye was considered the gateway to the
soul, and to the physician today, the eye serves as a window
through which the state of health can be readily observed.
Patrick D. Trevor Roper, *Lecture Notes in Ophthalmology*,
6th edition

There is one premise upon which physicians from
virtually every system of medicine the world over
agree – the eyes reveal many aspects relating to the state
of our health. Indeed, there are a great many medical disorders and diseases which can, in fact, be diagnosed from
markings in the eyes, and it is for this reason that the eyes
are considered by many doctors to be very important in
evaluating their patients' general health. In fact, as remarkable as it sounds, it has been estimated that the eyes reveal
over 3,000 different conditions relating to our physical
health.[1]

The Eyes – the First Signs of Health Problems

Signs of ill health are often seen in the eyes before any other
clinical symptoms appear. We have all seen how the eyes
become puffy and watery before the onset of 'flu, or how
the eyes appear smaller when we become tense or tired.
Every parent knows that one of the first signs of tiredness in
children is when they start rubbing their eyes. However, a

careful study of pathology soon reveals that the eyes are also the first organs in the body to be affected by many serious diseases and disorders.

In November 1994, a national English newspaper[2] reported a major breakthrough in detecting Alzheimer's disease. Scientists at Harvard Medical School discovered a simple test that could accurately diagnose Alzheimer's disease, a simple eye test.

Alzheimer's is a disease that afflicts over 700,000 people in the UK alone and causes degeneration of the brain cortex resulting in severe dementia including loss of memory, loss of speech and paralysis. Up until that time, there was no reliable way of diagnosing Alzheimer's disease. Although brain scans can indicate loss of brain cells, they cannot diagnose Alzheimer's and doctors had to rely on a series of psychological tests to try and predict whether patients had the disease. But the researchers demonstrated that they could accurately diagnose Alzheimer's in over 95 per cent of cases through the patients' eyes by observing the response of a patient's pupils to a highly-diluted drug. Dr Leonard Scinto, leader of the research team, explained: 'You get this very dramatic separation between patients with a clinical diagnosis of Alzheimer's and non-demented, healthy individuals.'

But Alzheimer's is only one of many diseases which can first be detected in the eyes. For instance, the first signs of jaundice are frequently seen by the whites of the eyes turning bright yellow. Diphtheria causes the pupils to dilate, whereas syphilis causes them to contract to pin-hole size, and paralysis of the eye muscles is the first indication of beri beri.

Chronic nephritis (persistent inflammation of the kidney) is often first diagnosed through the eyes – the eyelids become puffy and vision quickly deteriorates. Rheumatic fever and influenza are both commonly preceded by iritis (inflammation of the iris), and scarlet fever and measles usually begin with catarrhal conjunctivitis.

Diabetes is yet another disease whose symptoms

commonly first affect the eyes. Arterial disease is seen in the retinal arteries at the back of the eyes, and very often, new blood vessels appear in the iris (a condition known as 'rubieois iritis'). In fact, many diabetic patients are first made aware of their condition when they visit their optometrist after experiencing rapid deterioration of their vision.

The list of diseases that are commonly detected in the early stages through the eyes is endless. Little wonder, there-fore, that the eyes are considered to be an early warning mechanism in relation to our physical health. This is one reason why regular visits to your optometrist are so import-ant; a standard examination by a skilled optometrist can reveal information about your physical health which would be unavailable to your doctor without invasive diagnostic tests. In fact, an eye examination should be considered a necessary part of a general health check-up because it could identify health problems in their early stages and therefore provide the opportunity for effective preventive and re-medial treatment.

The earlier a disease can be diagnosed, the easier it is to treat. For instance, diabetes, high blood pressure and athero-sclerosis (hardening of the arteries caused by excess fat and cholesterol), can all be fatal if left undiagnosed and untreated. But, if diagnosed in their early stages, they can often be controlled and in many instances cured – without even resorting to medications – through simple dietary measures.

There are many health problems which are easily ident-ified in the eyes without the need of specialist equipment. Many of the markings and features in and around the eye reflect different matters relating to our health which can be seen every time we meet someone face-to-face.

Physical Constitution

There are several characteristics in and around the eyes that reveal information about the strength of a person's physical constitution. For instance, the masters of the ancient Chinese art of Siang Mien considered thick, strong eyebrows to be an indication of a strong constitution whereas thin eyebrows were believed to indicate a weak and delicate constitution.

It is the iris and the sclera, however, that give more detailed information about our general health. In iridology, the fibres in the iris are said to reflect the strength of the body tissues. The closer together the fibres appear, the stronger are the body tissues. So, fibres that are tight and closely knit together throughout the iris, as in Figure 3.1a, indicate a strong constitution. A person with these irises (known in iridology as 'silk' irises because of their likeness to silk cloth) often has superior energy levels, and is able to take on heavy workloads with the minimum need of rest and relaxation. It usually takes longer for these people to fall prey to illnesses and they have good recuperative abilities when they do become ill. On the down side, this type of iris reflects excess nervous energy and people with silk irises tend to be hyperactive and less able to relax.

Conversely, the irises of a person with a weak constitution have loosely-connected fibres giving the appearance of a net or spider's web as in Figure 3.1b. People with this type of iris are much more delicate and take much longer convalescing from physical illness. However, there is a positive side – people with 'net' irises tend to reveal a more relaxed disposition and are consequently far less susceptible to nervous tension.

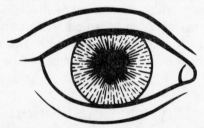

Figure 3.1a: Closely-knitted fibres in the iris indicating a strong constitution.

Figure 3.1b: Loosely-knitted fibres in the iris indicating a weak constitution.

The Heart, Circulatory Disorders and Cholesterol

Heart attacks are by far the largest single cause of death in all Western countries. They account for approximately 40 per cent of all deaths. Strokes account for another 10 per cent. What is the main cause of these deaths? A condition known as 'atherosclerosis' – accumulated fatty deposits forming plaque on the walls of the arteries which reduces the size of the openings through which blood can flow. If the arteries around the heart become affected, a heart attack occurs, whereas if the blood vessels in the brain become affected, it could give rise to a stroke.

Statistically, therefore, you and I are more likely to die prematurely from coronary heart disease than any other illness. In the USA, someone dies of a heart attack every 45 seconds, another person dies from a stroke every three minutes. In the UK, the situation is just as bad: over 900 people die every day from coronary heart disease – one person every 90 seconds!

In October 1990 the *American Journal of Public Health* reported a simple, inexpensive test which could be used to evaluate the risk of cardiovascular disease (e.g. heart disease, high blood pressure or stroke). The test, it said, should be considered just as useful as any conventional examination currently used to evaluate a person's risk of cardiovascular disease. The test to which the article referred was a simple examination of the eye.

35

It is well known, for instance, that hypercholesterolemia (excess serum cholesterol levels), a familial history of coronary heart disease, high blood pressure, obesity and smoking all increase the risk of cardiovascular disease. What is not so well-known is that the risk can be assessed by the markings and discolourations in the eye.

Nowhere on the body are blood vessels more easily observed than in the eye. The tiny blood vessels in the retina at the back of the eye are usually examined by your optician in a standard optometric examination. Peering through the pupil to the retina, the optician can identify many circulatory disorders including high blood pressure, arterial disease and excess cholesterol.

It is well accepted that most cases of coronary heart disease are preventable, especially when diagnosed in the early stages. Fortunately, the formative stages of many cardiovascular problems from atherosclerosis to high blood pressure are easily seen from markings in the eyes.

Hardening of the Arteries (atherosclerosis)

Hardening of the arteries is an extremely serious condition; insidious in its progress, it builds up over a period of years, often unnoticed, and can lead to high blood pressure, stroke or heart attack.

In 1988, an interesting story was reported in the *Listener* magazine.[3] A famous English actor, David Suchet, had been appearing on national television when an observant doctor, watching the programme, noticed something in Mr Suchet's eyes that indicated particularly severe hardening of the arteries. As Mr Suchet was, at the time, only in his late thirties, the doctor took it upon himself to write to him advising him of this diagnosis and suggesting that he have this looked into in more detail by his own doctor.

Mr Suchet, a self-confessed chocoholic, was somewhat alarmed by the letter he received and did consult his own doctor. Blood tests were taken which confirmed hypercholesterolemia (dangerously high levels of cholesterol in the blood) and Mr Suchet was immediately put on a restrictive diet which saved his life.

What had the observant doctor seen in Mr Suchet's eyes? A cholesterol ring (otherwise known as a sodium ring) – a whitish-yellow ring around the periphery of the iris *(see Figure 3.2)*. It is actually a cloudy discolouration caused by deposits on the cornea and it nonetheless indicates hardening of the arteries due to either excess cholesterol or mineral deposits formed on the arterial walls.

The cholesterol ring starts out as an arc at the top of the iris. This is known as an *arcus senilis* (literally translated as 'arc of old age') because it is commonly seen in elderly people. However, recent research has confirmed what iridologists have known for the past century: the arcus senilis indicates hardening of the arteries due to an accumulation of plaque made up of cholesterol or mineral deposits which could, if untreated, lead to a stroke in people of any age.

As the condition progresses, another arc forms at the bottom of the iris before the circle in the iris is completed, revealing an advanced condition throughout the body. The thicker the ring, the more severe the condition *(see Figure 3.3)*.

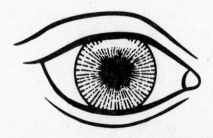

Figure 3.2: The arcus senilis – early stages of arterio/ atherosclerosis (hardening of the arteries).

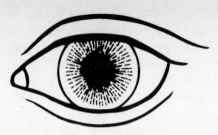

Figure 3.3: The sodium/cholesterol ring – a sign of high cholesterol levels, arterio/atherosclerosis (hardening of the arteries) and a greater risk of coronary heart disease.

There have been two interesting medical studies done on the arcus senilis and cholesterol ring, both of which verified their relationship with cardio-vascular diseases.

In November 1987, the *Los Angeles Herald Examiner* reported the findings of an eight-year study conducted by the National Heart, Lung and Blood Institute. The study revealed that men under the age of 50 who had an arcus senilis in their eyes had over double the risk of having a heart attack. The risk was further increased by four times if the men also had excess cholesterol levels in the blood *(see below)*.

In another study reported in the January 1990 edition of the *Journal of the American Optometric Association*, researchers found that there was a direct correlation – regardless of age – between an arcus senilis/cholesterol ring and high serum cholesterol levels. The researchers discovered that people who had an arcus senilis or cholesterol ring in their eyes had significantly higher serum cholesterol levels than people whose eyes did not have an arcus senilis or cholesterol ring.

In a healthy person, normal serum cholesterol levels are below 150mg/dl (i.e. 150mg per decilitre). Anything above that figure is considered to represent an increased risk of coronary heart disease, and the higher the levels rise, the greater the risk. The researchers found that approximately nine out of every ten people (88 per cent) who have an arcus senilis or cholesterol ring in their eyes have serum cholesterol levels above 200mg/dl, whereas only 33 per cent of people who did not have an arcus senilis or cholesterol ring had such high serum cholesterol levels.

It should therefore come as no surprise to learn that most people who have an arcus senilis or cholesterol ring in their eyes will invariably have had a diet containing a lot of fatty foods and high cholesterol (e.g. meats, dairy food, chocolates and fried food). It is important, if these markings are seen in the eyes, that all such foods are eliminated from the diet.[4]

Whilst there is a strong correlation between an arcus senilis and cholesterol ring with elevated serum cholesterol levels, it is important to note that this is not always the case. This is because the arcus senilis and cholesterol ring reveal arterial disease – hardening, narrowing and degeneration of the arteries due to accumulated cholesterol and/or mineral deposits forming on the arterial walls and not the concentration of cholesterol levels in the blood.

This distinction is important because some people may have high serum cholesterol levels but no arcus senilis where, for example, no cholesterol deposits have yet formed on the arterial walls. Conversely, a person may have an arcus senilis in their eyes but normal serum cholesterol levels. This is because serum cholesterol levels can be reduced very quickly, within eight weeks, by adopting a low fat, high fibre diet[5] but it takes much longer for the body to break up and eliminate those deposits which may have accumulated over a period of years and formed on the walls of the arteries.

Cholesterol Problems Seen in the Sclera

Excess serum cholesterol levels are also indicated by yellow fatty deposits in the whites of the eyes or on the eyelids themselves. Raised yellow patches in the sclera (known as 'pingueculae') can form on either side of the iris as illustrated in Figure 3.4. They can be caused by prolonged exposure to wind and sunlight, although Mr David Dhooma, a contact lens practitioner with over 25 years' experience, advises that pingueculae are often a preliminary warning sign of problems with cholesterol metabolism. In some cases, a triangular, bulbous, yellow lesion forms on the sclera which invades the iris (known as a 'pterygium') seen in Figure 3.5. Whilst these are augmented in hot, dusty climates they are also in essence a lipid formation revealing potential problems with fat and cholesterol metabolism.

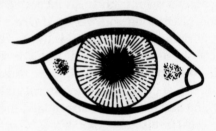

Figure 3.4: Pingueculae – possible early warning of cholesterol problems.

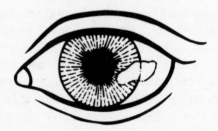

Figure 3.5: Pterigium – possible early warning of cholesterol problems.

Cholesterol Problems Seen in the Eyelids

It is not uncommon to see people who have yellow patches or nodules on their upper and/or lower eyelids as in Figure 3.6. These are known as 'xanthelasma' and are very easily seen. They are, in fact, lumps of cholesterol and indicate

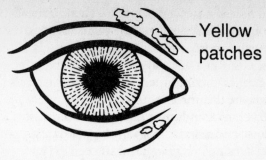

Yellow
patches

*Figure 3.6: Xanthelasma – yellow patches on the eyelids
indicating problems with cholesterol metabolism.*

high serum cholesterol levels and a problem with cholesterol metabolism.

High Blood Pressure

Blood pressure is most accurately and very easily monitored by
your doctor using a standard stethoscope and sphygmo-
manometer, however there are several indicators of high blood
pressure in the eyes. As mentioned above, atheroscler-osis seen
as an arcus senilis or cholesterol ring causes a narrowing of the
arteries which can lead to high blood pressure.

High blood pressure can also cause the blood vessels in
the whites of the eyes to become prominent. In such a case
a mass of blood vessels are seen throughout the sclera. It

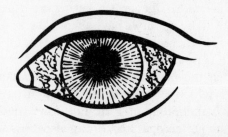

Figure 3.7: Prominent blood vessels throughout the sclera.

41

should be noted, however, that eye irritations or infections such as conjunctivitis will have the same effect on the blood vessels. Furthermore, prominent blood vessels should be distinguished from a general reddening of the sclera which is considered by practitioners of traditional Chinese medicine to indicate liver problems.

A more accurate indicator of high blood pressure is seen from a cluster of circular rings in the iris (known as 'stress rings', 'tension rings' or 'cramp rings'), seen in Figure 3.8. The stress rings indicate an accumulation of mental or physical stress and they have also been associated with high blood pressure and cardiovascular problems. One researcher found that 66 per cent of people who had stress rings in their eyes also suffered from high blood pressure or cardiac disorders.[6]

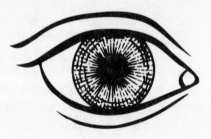

Figure 3.8: Stress rings in the iris.

Stroke

A cerebral haemorrhage or stroke occurs when a blood vessel bursts in the brain. We have already discussed how the eyes reveal whether a person is more at risk from having a stroke by the appearance of an arcus senilis or cholesterol ring, and that the eyes also record high stress levels *(see Chapter 4)* which is an additional causative factor, but the eyes also accurately indicate not only whether or not someone has suffered a stroke but also how severe the stroke may have been.

When a doctor arrives on the scene of an accident, the first thing he will examine (after ensuring that the patient has a pulse and is breathing) will be the patient's eyes. This is because the eyes will tell the doctor if the patient's brain has been seriously affected. If a stroke has occurred, the pupil in one eye becomes *severely* dilated as in Figure 3.9. The doctor will even know which *side* of the brain has suffered a haemorrhage – the left eye records the right side of the brain and the right eye records the left side of the brain.

Occasionally, you may see people who have one pupil which is slightly larger than the other. This does not necessarily mean that they have had a stroke, but it does indicate that there is an imbalance in their nervous system. The greater the disparity between the sizes of the pupils, the greater the neurological damage.

Serious disorders relating to the nervous system can be seen when a person's pupils do not react to changes in light. If, for instance, a bright light is shone on a person's eyes, you should see the pupils contract instantly. They do this to protect the eyeball by preventing too much light entering and damaging the retina. Similarly, in dimly lit rooms, the pupils will be seen to dilate to allow more light to enter the eyeball and help us see more clearly. If one or both of the pupils do not react in this way, but will adjust in size when a person focuses on an object, it is an indication of a diseased nervous system. The condition is known as 'Argyll-Robertson' pupils and indicates neurological damage resulting in an imbalance in the functioning of the nervous system.

Figure 3.9: Unequal-sized pupils indicating neurological damage and possible stroke.

Varicose Veins

The term 'varicose veins' describes the condition in which veins dilate due to the degeneration of the valves inside them. The incompetent veins are no longer able to resist the gravitational force exerted on the blood and, as a result, the flow of blood travels backwards down the leg or stagnates, causing the veins to bulge.

Whilst there are many factors thought to be associated with varicose veins (including a sedentary lifestyle, pregnancy, obesity, excessive exposure to sunlight, smoking, constipation, certain sports activities involving water – especially canoeing and kayaking – poor nutrition, a high fat/ low fibre diet), there is also a strong hereditary influence. One clinical study found that the risk of developing varicose veins for children was 90 per cent when both parents suffered from this disease, 25 per cent for males and 62 per cent for females when one parent was affected, and 20 per cent of both males and females when neither parent was affected.[7]

Fortunately, the eyes often give an early warning of this condition and therefore allow preventive action to be taken to stop the problem deteriorating.

If you look closely at the position of six o'clock in each iris, you can see the general condition of the veins in each leg. If there is a hole (known as a 'lacuna') beneath the wreath as in Figure 3.10 there is a tendency to varicose veins in the same leg. The deeper the hole, the worse the condition of the veins.

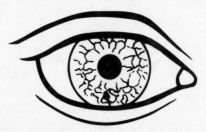

Figure 3.10: Lacuna (hole) at six o'clock, indicating a tendency to varicose veins

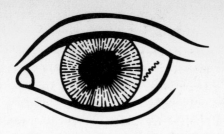

Figure 3.11: Sclera blood vessel indicating varicose veins.

Another indication of varicose veins is seen from the blood vessels in the whites of the eyes. If the vessels are shaped as in Figure 3.11 varicosity in the veins is indicated.

Whenever varicose veins are suspected, it is important to take excessive strain off the veins. For instance, fatty food thickens the blood and causes greater pressure on the veins. Standing for long periods also aggravates the condition as the gravitational force put pressure on the veins. It is therefore advisable:

a) to keep the legs elevated whenever possible
b) not to cross the legs at the knee because this restricts blood flow in the lower leg
c) not to eat high-fat foods (e.g. meat, fatty cheeses, chocolates, etc)
d) do regular daily exercise, as the only thing that forces the blood up through the veins is muscle contraction. Light, brisk walking or swimming are ideal.

Poor Circulation and Skin Problems

It is well known that people with light-coloured eyes tend to have more sensitive skin than people with dark-coloured eyes. However, it was not until the results were published of the first National Health and Nutrition Examination Survey[8] in the United States that scientists had evidence confirming that people with light-coloured eyes had a much greater incidence of skin cancers and associated degenerative, ageing

45

skin conditions, as well as eye damage from exposure to ultra-violet radiation, than dark-eyed people.

Researchers discovered that people with light eyes are significantly more susceptible than dark-eyed people to a host of skin conditions known to be related to excessive exposure to ultraviolet radiation (e.g. wrinkled skin, senile lentigines and freckles, hypermelanism – excess pigmentation – liver spots and melanomas). This is presumably because people with light-coloured eyes are not able to produce the protective skin pigment 'melanin' as efficiently as dark-eyed people. Consequently, it is now accepted that light-eyed people need to take extra care of their skin if they are to avoid these types of skin problems.

Poor Circulation Seen in the Eyes

A tendency to cold extremities and minor skin complaints such as eczema, dermatitis and psoriasis is seen by markings in the periphery of the iris. If the periphery appears fuzzy and indistinct, the circulation is poor but, as the condition worsens, a dark ring appears around the very outer edge of the iris (known as a 'scurf rim') as in Figure 3.12. The scurf rim reveals an underfunctioning skin which often leads to problems with perspiration, as well as sluggish circulation.

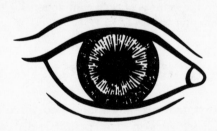

Figure 3.12: Scurf rim – darkened periphery indicating poor circulation and tendency to skin complaints.

Consequently, people with a scurf rim in their irises, more often than not, suffer from minor skin complaints as well as cold hands and feet. The darker and thicker the rim appears, the more chronic will be the person's condition.

People with this marking therefore need to stimulate the skin through regular physical exercise sufficient to induce perspiration, dry skin brushing, saunas and steam baths.

Digestive Disorders

Acid Indigestion

Acid indigestion and ulcerative conditions in the stomach and intestines are often present when there is white discolouration or a silver halo around the pupil *(see Figure 3.13)*. A build up of acid can be caused by eating too many acid-forming food (e.g. meats, hard cheeses, peanuts, citrus fruit, bread and cakes, sugary foods, cooked tomatoes, coffee, tea and alcohol), medications (e.g. aspirin irritates the stomach membrane and is known to cause gastro-intestinal bleeding in three quarters of the people who regularly use it) and, of course, stress.

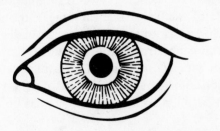

Figure 3.13: Acid halo – white ring around the pupil indicating hyperacidity in the stomach and intestines.

Irritable Bowels and Constipation

When you look closely at someone's eyes you can actually see whether they have a tendency to irritable bowels or

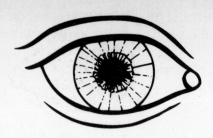

Figure 3.14:The wreath in the iris reveals the shape and condition of the intestines.

constipation.The wreath shown in Figure 3.14 corresponds exactly to the condition and shape of their intestines. Dr Bernard Jensen researched this marking in the iris comparing the wreath in patients' eyes with X-rays of their large intestines.[9] The results were remarkable, with even bowel pockets being accurately identified through the displacement of the wreath in the iris.

The detail with which you can observe someone's intestines through their eyes is quite astounding. In my own practice I was consulted by a man whose eyes indicated an obstruction in his descending colon.He admitted having been constipated and that he had been in some pain,but he had had two X-rays and a U-scan only a few weeks earlier which had shown nothing abnormal. The following day he had an appointment with a consultant at the hospital,at which it was decided that a coloscopy (a detailed examination of his colon and rectum by microscopic camera) should be carried out.

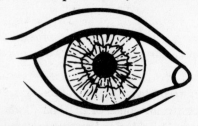

Figure 3.15:A jagged wreath indicating a spastic colon and likely irritable bowel syndrome.

Figure 3.16:A wreath close to the pupil indicates tension and a tendency to constipation.

This detailed examination confirmed that there was indeed a blockage in the descending colon – it was, in fact, a malignant tumour which required emergency treatment.

Irritable bowels are indicated when the wreath in the eye is irregular as in Figure 3.15. In this case, the person has a spastic colon (i.e. sections of the colon are in spasm) and as a result bowel movements become irregular, alternating between diarrhoea and constipation.

When the wreath is close to the pupil, as in Figure 3.16, it indicates that the intestines are in spasm throughout and as a result bowel movements become restricted, leading to constipation.

Both of these conditions can be caused by a lack of fibre in the diet as well as mental stress and emotional tension. Constipation is commonly associated by holistic health practitioners with an inability to let go of past hurts, memories or even of material possessions and money.[10]

Gall Bladder Problems

The gall bladder is really just a small sac which stores bile and secretes it into the duodenum (first section of the small intestines) to help digest fats. Problems start to occur when we eat excessive amounts of high-fat foods as this puts a strain on the gall bladder and cholesterol deposits can crystallize into stones in the gall bladder. If these stones can be

49

caught early enough, they can be broken down through ultrasound therapy or eliminated naturopathically using herbs and dietary changes. However, if the stones become too large, they can cause the most intense pain (comparable, I am told, only to the pain of childbirth) and by this time surgical removal of the gall bladder is often advised.

The gall bladder is recorded in the right iris at the position of eight o'clock as in Figure 3.17. If this area appears white, the gall bladder will be inflamed, if it appears brown or black, it will be chronically affected. However, the iris is not able to

Figure 3.17: The position of the gall bladder in the iris.

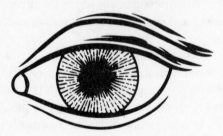

Figure 3.18: Swollen or darkened upper eyelids indicate gall bladder problems.

reveal whether or not there are gallstones present. The iris only reveals the condition of the body tissues and therefore if gallstones are present but not causing any irritation or inflammation, no abnormalities will appear in the iris.

Practitioners of traditional Chinese medicine identify gall bladder problems by a bulging or darkening of the upper eyelids.

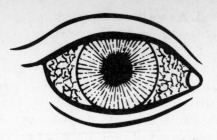

*Figure 3.19a: Concentration of red blood vessels in the sclera –
indication of possible kidney problems.*

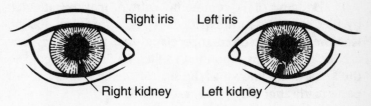

Figure 3.19b: The position of the kidneys in the iris.

Kidney Problems

The first sign of kidney problems is seen when there is a
concentration of red blood vessels in the sclera (see Figure
3.19a). This is why people's eyes commonly appear red
after they have had too much alcohol to drink.

Another indication of more serious kidney problems is
seen by a darkening or bulging of the lower eyelid as in

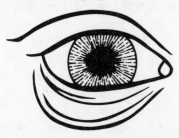

*Figure 3.20: Swollen or darkened lower eyelids
indicate kidney problems.*

Figure 3.19b. It makes them look tired, haggard and in need of rest. What it actually means, according to Chinese medicine, is that the person has kidney problems. This can be confirmed by taking a close look in the iris; the kidney areas are situated between five and six o'clock in the right eye and six and seven o'clock in the left iris where, if the kidneys are inflamed (nephritis) the area will appear white (except in a brown eye where it will appear a very light brown) and if there is a chronic or long-standing problem the area will appear a much darker colour than the rest of the iris.

The kidneys, it is commonly known, may be affected by diet (e.g. acid-forming foods – *see above*) or alcohol. However, it is not often appreciated that the kidneys may also be affected by emotions. In fact, in Chinese medicine the kidneys are known as the seat of the emotions and are particularly affected by fear and anxiety.

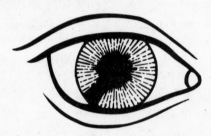

Figure 3.21: The position of the liver in the iris.

Liver Problems and Jaundice

The liver is recorded in the right iris between the position of 7.45–8 o'clock as in Figure 3.21. This area will appear white if the liver is inflamed or dark if there are chronic (long-term) problems.

When the whites of the eyes appear yellow, jaundice is usually suspected. This is a sign that is also common to many animals including dogs and cats, and if you have a pet whose eyes look yellowish, it is a good idea to take the animal to a vet for a thorough check-up.

When the sclera appears red in colour – without prominent blood vessels which indicate an eye infection or high blood pressure – it is considered by traditional Chinese medical practitioners to be a sign of an underfunctioning or troublesome liver.

Wherever a problem with the liver is suspected, it is advisable to avoid alcohol, sugary foods and fatty foods, because all of these put unnecessary strain on the liver.

Nutritional Deficiencies

Most of the time we have to wait until we experience certain symptoms before we become aware that we might be lacking certain nutrients. For instance, we will often become lethargic and fatigued and our complexions appear pale before we realize that we may be anaemic. We develop brittle bones when we lack sufficient calcium and a low intake of iodine can lead to an underfunctioning thyroid gland. Amazingly, one look at our eyes is often all it takes to see whether we are beginning to lack certain nutrients.

Anaemia – Lack of Iron

Anaemia – lack of iron in the blood – can cause listlessness, tiredness and lethargy. Sometimes, a lack of iron can even cause our hair to fall out. Fortunately, anaemia is very easily identified from the eyes whilst still in its early stages.

Anaemia can be seen from the colour of the inside of the lower eyelid. In a healthy person it should have a red, fleshly appearance. This is because the blood vessels under the lower eyelid are the most easily seen anywhere in the body (without the need of any special equipment) and it is the iron which gives the haemoglobin in the blood its red colour. Lack of iron means lack of red, fleshy colour. When anaemia is present the flesh turns very pale and in severe cases, almost white.

The inside of the eyelid should appear a pink, fleshy colour. If it is pale/white it indicates anaemia.

Figure 3.22: Pale flesh on the inner eyelid – an indication of anaemia.

If anaemia is suspected, it is advisable to look carefully at your diet and make sure you are eating plenty of green leafy vegetables, especially broccoli, molasses, prunes, brewer's yeast, rolled oats, raisins, and even dark chocolate! (Go easy on the chocolate because it also contains a lot of fat and sugar.) Remember also to eat plenty of fresh fruits because vitamin C helps the body absorb iron more easily.

Lack of Calcium – Osteoporosis and Osteogenesis Imperfecta

Osteogenesis imperfecta is a disease in which the bones are not formed sufficiently due to an inability to utilize calcium effectively. This can therefore lead to osteoporosis (brittle bones).

An X-ray will only show degeneration of bone tissue in osteoporosis after a minimum of thirty per cent of the bone mass has been lost. Bone scans are far more accurate but due to their expense they are only suggested when a patient has developed related symptoms. The eyes, on the other hand, often give the first indication of any problems. One of the first signs of osteogenesis imperfecta and thus a tendency to osteoporosis is that the whites of the eyes appear blue.

Lack of Iodine – Hypothyroidism

It is now commonly accepted that a lack of iodine or insufficient metabolism of iodine is related to disease of the thyroid gland and this is another condition commonly diagnosed through the eyes.

It was a physician named Karl von Basedow who, back in the nineteenth century, was credited with the discovery that a deficiency of iodine led to overactivity of the thyroid gland

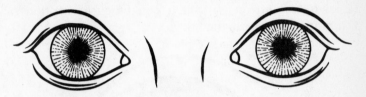

Figure 3.23: Bulging, protruding eyes – a sign of goitre.

Figure 3.24: The position of the thyroid gland in the iris.

(goitre) and produced wide, bulging, protruding eyes. However, Chinese medicine has stated for thousands of years that bulging eyes indicate problems with the thyroid gland.

Problems with the thyroid gland can also be confirmed in the irises by a darkening in the region of two to three o'clock in the right iris and nine to ten o'clock in the left iris as in Figure 3.24.

The thyroid gland controls the general metabolism (i.e. conversion of food into energy) in the body and consequently problems with the thyroid gland can lead to weight gain or loss (depending upon whether it is over or underactive) and lethargy. If the disease can be alerted early enough, preventative nutritional measures can be taken which will often correct the condition without resorting to drugs or surgery. For instance, seaweed or iodized sea salt are rich sources of iodine, and raw cabbage, turnips and peanuts should be avoided as these contain natural substances (known as goitre-gens) which can block absorption or utilization of iodine in the body.

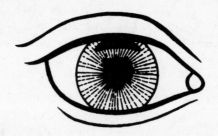

Figure 3.25:A copper-coloured arc – a sign of Wilson's disease.

Copper

Poor copper metabolism is a relatively rare disorder known as 'Wilson's disease' in which copper accumulates in the liver and brain. This is another disorder that can be diagnosed in the eyes.

The marking in the eye indicating Wilson's disease appears like a copper-coloured arc (known as a 'Kayser-Fleischner ring') at the top of the iris as in Figure 3.25.

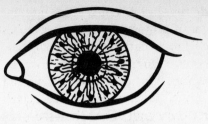

*Figure 3.26:A rosary around the outer section of the iris –
a tendency to allergies, hay fever, oedema and infections.*

Allergies, Hay Fever and a Lowered Immune System

A tendency to allergies, hay fever and an impaired immune system is seen in the iris of the eyes in the form of puffy clouds around the outer section of the iris as in Figure 3.26. The clouds are known as a 'lymphatic rosary' and indicate a congested lymphatic system, and the darker they appear, the more chronic will be the condition.

The lymphatic system is the waste disposal unit of the body. All cellular waste is collected in the lymphatic vessels and carried toward the lymph nodes in the groin, neck, armpits and abdomen where germs and bacteria are destroyed. If the lymphatic system is congested it is, in effect, under-functioning and the body's cellular waste is not being efficiently eliminated. As a result, people with a congested lymphatic system become prone to allergies, hay fever, infections and fluid retention.

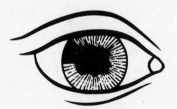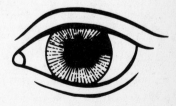

Figure 3.27:The position of the lungs and bronchials in the iris.

The main causes of congested lymph are shallow breathing, lack of physical exercise and excessive amounts of meat, dairy foods, chocolates, sweets, cakes and sugary drinks in the diet.

Respiratory and Bronchial Disorders

Dark patches in the right iris between nine and ten o'clock and in the left eye between two and three o'clock indicate weak lungs and therefore a tendency to asthma, bronchitis and other respiratory disorders. If these areas appear white, it is showing inflammation of the lungs and bronchials and the person will almost certainly be suffering from a chest complaint.

Figure 3.28: Non-reactive pin-hole pupils – a sign of narcotic abuse or syphilis.

Syphilis and Narcotic Abuse

Syphilis is yet another disease commonly diagnosed from the eyes. This very serious venereal disease causes the pupils to become pin-point in size and non-reactive to light. High doses of narcotics such as morphine also have the same effect. Fortunately, it is not something you will be likely to see very often.

Cataract and Glaucoma

Cataract and glaucoma, if untreated, can both cause blindness. Both may be diagnosed in their early stages in a standard optical examination. In their later stages, both can easily be seen by the colour of the pupil in the eyes. In cataract, metabolic waste forms deposits on the lens in the eye and this gives the pupil a cloudy, grey colour.

In glaucoma, pressure builds up in the eyeball and this will also create a clouding of the pupil, usually with a tinge of green. In advanced stages, the clouding extends over the cornea and can cover much of the iris.

Endnotes

1. Professor J. Liberman OD, PhD *Light: medicine of the future,* Bear & Co, 1991, p.14.
2. *Daily Mail,* Friday 11 November 1994.
3. 5 May 1998, p.21.
4. For specific dietary measures – see (5) below.
5. See Cox, P. and Brusseau, P., *The Quick Cholesterol Clean-Out,* Centry Hutchinson Ltd, 1989.
6. Rafal Korvin-Swiecki reported by Jessica Maxwell in *The Eye-body Connection,* Warner, 1980.
7. Cornu-Thenard, A., Boivin, P., Baud, J. M., De Vincenzi, I., Carpentier, P. H., 'Importance of the familial factor in varicose disease. Clinical study of 134 families' Service de Cardiologie, Hopital Saint-Antoine, Paris, France, *Journal of Dermatologic Surgery & Oncology* (US) May 1994, 20 (5), pp.318–26.
8. Engel, A., Johnson, M. L., Haynes, S. G., 'Health effects of sunlight exposure in the United States. Results from the first National Health and Nutrition Examination Survey, 1971–1974' Medical Statistics Branch, National Center for Health Statistics, Hyattsville, MD 20892, *Archives of Dermatology* (US) Jan 1988, 124 (1), pp.72–9.
9. Jensen, B., *The Science and Practice of Iridology,* pp.307–31, B. Jensen, 1952.
10. See L. Hay, *Heal your Body: The mental causes for physical illness and the metaphysical way to overcome them,* Heaven on Earth Books, 1985.

CHAPTER 4

Stress in the Eyes

There are often voices and words in a silent look.
Ovid

Stress is a necessary part of life; without it there is no growth. Physical stress builds muscle power, mental stress develops the mind, and emotional stress nurtures the spirit. But, if stress accumulates and becomes unmanageable, it can be extremely damaging to our mental and physical health. In fact, stress is said to account for many health problems including heart disease, hair loss, indigestion, migraine, skin problems and even cancer. Fortunately, physical, mental and emotional stresses can all be monitored in the eyes.

Stress – A Cause of Poor Vision

Stress is now acknowledged to be a major cause of poor eyesight. Dr Bates stated that mental strain is the main factor in all defects of vision because it causes corresponding physical strain upon the eyes and their muscles and nerves which, in turn, distorts the vision.

Dr Bates believed that a highly nervous temperament is often a precipitating factor in many visual disorders, and that mental tension is a major cause in most cases of serious visual deficiency. Even minor visual problems (e.g. myopia – short-

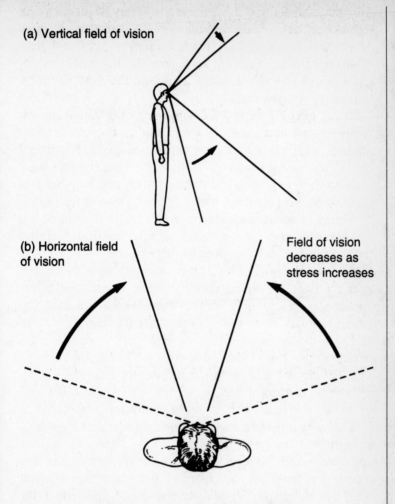

(a) Vertical field of vision

(b) Horizontal field of vision

Field of vision decreases as stress increases

Figure 4.1: Stress and the field of vision.

sightedness – and hypermetropia – long-sightedness) were seen, by Dr Bates, as the effect of mental strain resulting from worry, anxiety, fear and overwork.[1] Consequently, an important part of the process that Dr Bates developed to improve eyesight revolved around relaxation exercises.

Whilst conventional opticians at the turn of the century

ridiculed and scoffed at Dr Bates's theories, in recent years researchers have vindicated his views. For instance, a series of studies conducted by Mark Anderson PhD and Jean Williams PhD revealed that stress directly affects our peripheral field of vision.[2] As stress increases, the field of vision reduces proportionately.

One optician I interviewed witnessed a significant clinical improvement in a patient's vision within the space of 20 minutes which he could only explain by the alleviation of stress. The patient was particularly nervous during her sight test and so the optician had decided to try and help her feel more at ease by chatting with her over a cup of tea before continuing the sight examination. When he continued his examination, the optician was amazed to find that the patient's vision had improved by 80 per cent!

Noise pollution, another form of stress, also affects our eyes. In 1931 an article entitled 'Noise Causes Bad Eyes' appeared in the science journal *Popular Science Monthly* which reported the work of Professor P. P. Lazarev and Dr L. Kuper in Russia investigating the effect of loud noises on a person's sight. It was found that city dwellers tended to have significantly worse eyesight than country folk and the researchers concluded that the continuous noise in the city from road and railway traffic was a determining factor.[3]

When any form of stress – emotional, mental or physical – accumulates uncontrollably and we feel that we cannot cope, our health suffers. Sometimes, we try to hide the fact that we cannot cope with a stress from our bosses or loved ones. But, if the stress accumulates it will, in time, affect our work or our health – or both. Fortunately, there are easily recognizable signs in the eyes that tell us how stress is affecting a person and when they need help.

Stress Seen in the Eyes

Stress affects both the functioning and appearance of the eyes. Specific, easily recognizable markings and signs appear in and around the eyes that reveal if someone feels stressed, or if they have been under prolonged stress, and even whether they have a nervous disposition. There are signs that show whether someone has recent worries and anxiety or chronic emotional problems, and there are markings that indicate whether a person may be suffering from nervous exhaustion or even post-traumatic stress disorder. All these conditions are seen in the pupil, the iris, the sclera and the eye movements.

The Pupil and the Nervous System

The size and shape of the pupils in our eyes are controlled by light; if we are in bright sunlight, the pupils automatically contract to prevent too much light entering the eyeball and causing damage to the retina. Conversely, in dimly-lit environments, our pupils dilate to allow more light to enter the eyeball and so help us to see more clearly. However, the pupils are not only controlled by light, they are also directly affected by our central nervous system.

We have already seen how unequal-sized pupils are a sign of an imbalanced nervous system and how a person who has suffered a stroke will have one pupil significantly dilated *(see Chapter 3)*. Narcotic and stimulant drugs also affect the pupil; cocaine, belladonna, atropin drugs will cause the pupil to dilate whereas narcotics such as opium and heroine will cause the pupils to contract. All major changes in the brain and nervous system will instantaneously affect the pupils in the eyes and it is for this very reason that researchers are now able, using sophisticated equipment, to diagnose neurological disorders through pupilliary reactions to controlled stimuli.[4]

Physical Pain and Mental Stress

In normal light, the pupils should appear approximately 3mm in diameter, about one third of the size of the iris. Certain emotions (e.g. disgust and revulsion – *see Chapter*

5) can temporarily cause the pupils to contract, but if the pupils appear noticeably smaller over a period of hours or days, they are indicating current physical or mental stress caused by drugs, pain or mental tension. This is why people who are under stress appear to have small eyes.

Figure 4.2: Contracted pupils.

Nervous Exhaustion

When the pupils are dilated in normal lighting, they are indicating nervous exhaustion which again may be caused by drugs or prolonged physical or mental stress. The greater the dilation, the larger the pupils appear, which indicates that the condition is more serious. Many people with dilated pupils are only able to get through the day with the aid of stimulants such as caffeine, nicotine or sugary foods, but their eyes will always reveal how they are really coping inside.

Figure 4.3: Dilated pupils.

It should, however, be noted that certain emotions (e.g. physical attraction – *see Chapter 8*, and excitement – *see Chapter 5*) can also *temporarily* dilate the pupils. This is because physical attraction often produces a temporary depletion of nervous energy, a feeling of being 'weak at the knees'!

Accumulated Stress and Hypertension

A person who has accumulated stress over a period of years or who naturally has a nervous disposition, will have specific markings in their eyes known as 'tension rings'. These are circular rings that appear in their irises as in Figure 3.7. The more rings present, the greater the accumulated stress. In this day and age, one or two are quite normal, more than that is not and indicates that the person finds it difficult to deal with the stresses and strains in their life.

Stress rings therefore indicate that a person has difficulty handling stressful situations. The person is often seen by others to be a 'nervous' type, easily fretful or tense. When, for instance, two people are travelling on a train which is delayed, making them late for work, the person with stress rings in his eyes is pulling his hair out and bursting a few blood vessels, whereas the other person may be able to accept the situation, realizing that there is nothing he can do about it, and go back to reading his paper.

One study revealed that over 75 per cent of people with more than four stress rings in their eyes suffered with hypertension. In my practice, I have even seen young children with numerous tension rings and in every case there has been conflict between the parents in the home or problems at school. Children are very perceptive of tension in their surroundings and the earlier the cause of their tension is identified, the better it will of course be for the emotional development of the child.

Anxiety and Worry

Anxiety and worry are seen in the eyes although they are not always easy to spot, due to the fact that the marking lies in the top half of the iris and is consequently often covered by the upper eyelid.

The area between 11 o'clock and 1 o'clock in each iris relates to the brain. When there are white flares in this region from the nerve wreath outwards, as in Figure 4.4, it reveals that the person has a lot on their mind. This is commonly seen in the eyes of students studying hard for exams, mothers whose children are not well and business men and women struggling to meet deadlines. Of the thousands of people who have come through my clinic, everyone who has had this marking is troubled by worries and anxiety.

If the worries persist, the flares turn yellow, then orange and then brown. The darker the discolouration, the more chronic the problems, which sometimes may even reach back into childhood. Whenever someone has dark brown flares between 11 o'clock and 1 o'clock in their irises, they will have deep-rooted, unresolved emotional conflicts and are often in need of counselling or therapy.

Figure 4.4: White flares between 11 o'clock and 1 o'clock in the iris reveal anxiety and worry.

Figure 4.5: Dark flares between 11 o'clock and 12 o'clock in the iris reveal deep-rooted, unresolved emotional conflicts.

Once the source of the tension or conflict has been eliminated, the tension rings will begin to fade, and the flares in the upper section of the iris will start to disappear.

Eye Movements and Post-Traumatic Stress Disorder

In 1987, a young psychology student was walking through a Californian park when she stumbled across a discovery which may well have led to one of the most significant breakthroughs this century in clinical psychology. Like most medical advances, it came from a chance observation of the positive association between the way we move our eyes and emotional or mental stress, but more significantly it led to a revolutionary new mode of treatment for post-traumatic stress disorder.

As she walked through the park, Francine Shapiro's mind was preoccupied with disturbing thoughts but she suddenly became aware that her eyes were jerking, moving involuntarily from side to side. To her astonishment, when the movements finally stopped, her recollection of those unpleasant memories which had troubled her became less clear and no longer upset her. 'Could it be,' she asked herself, 'that the movement of our eyes is linked in some way to hidden psychological stresses?'

Subsequent clinical research confirmed her suspicions – our eye movements are intrinsically related to mental and emotional stress. Since that time, other researchers have demonstrated how psychological disorders, including schizophrenia, depression and alexithymia, affect our eye movements *(see Chapters 5 and 6)*. Ms Shapiro was able to take her findings one stage further; she found that patients suffering from post-traumatic stress disorder (including those traumatized by assaults, road accidents and bereavements), as well as anxiety-based disorders, phobias and depression, could be effectively *treated* through management of their eye movements.

The technique Ms Shapiro called 'Eye Movement Desensitization and Reprocessing' (EMDR) was first taken seriously by the scientific community after a leading psychology journal published an article by respected psychologists[5] and is thought to be a revolutionary new mode of treatment for many forms of mental illness with over 4,000 clinical psychologists using the technique worldwide.

The EMDR technique is itself very simple and principally involves the patient following specific exercises in their eye movements under the supervision of a trained therapist, whilst simultaneously recalling past traumas in their minds. There is no hypnosis, no trance; it is simply a question of consciously controlling the eye movements and this affects the subconscious and has the power to change our perceptions of past traumas.

It sounds incredible, almost unbelievable, but the results of controlled research studies into EMDR are nothing short of remarkable. In the Veterans Affairs Medical Center, North Chicago, Vietnam war veterans suffering from severe post-traumatic stress disorder experienced marked decreases in the distress associated with severely troubling memories after only one session of EMDR.[6] The men reported a diminution of the visual aspect of the troubling memories that had haunted them for over 15 years. It was the first time that any treatment procedure had had such an effect on the men.

A report from the Department of Psychology at the Western Washington University tells a similar story: a 40-year-old man had been suffering from post-traumatic stress disorder for over eight years following an incident in which he had been attacked and shot with a pistol. EMDR treatment quickly desensitized the patient to the experience and it emerged that he had also been the victim of two earlier attacks and these traumas were also desensitized. The patient himself noticed the changes brought about by the treatment, and psychiatric evaluations pre and post treatment confirmed that the condition had been completely cured.[7]

Mr John Spector, consultant clinical psychologist and head of Adult Mental Health at Watford General Hospital, England, for more than ten years is one of the leading exponents of EMDR in the Europe. Mr Spector stated that 'in relation to post-traumatic stress disorder it [EMDR] is the most effective and quickest treatment method I have ever come across'. He went on to explain, 'Patients who had suffered post-traumatic stress disorder for 23 years and been in therapy for six years were, after only one 60 minute session of EMDR symptom-free.' Through EMDR patients with post-traumatic stress disorders are able to completely change their views of themselves and their experiences.

The benefits of EMDR far outweigh drug therapy according to Mr Spector because drug therapy can only treat the symptoms. 'As soon as a patient comes off the drugs,' said Mr Spector, 'the cause of the problem remains. EMDR deals with those causes.'

Endnotes

1. Benjamin, H., *Better Sight Without Glasses*, Health for All Publishing Co, 1929.
2. Anderson, M. D. and Williams, J.M., 'Seeing too straight; stress and vision', *Longevity*, Aug 1989.
3. April 1931 p.33.
4. Waldorf, R., 'The Use of Eye Performance Tests for Evaluation of Vestibular and Neurological Function, Including Central Nervous System Impairment from Alcohol and Drugs', 26 September 1994, private paper.
5. Wolpe, J., and Abrams, J., 'Post traumatic stress disorder overcome by eye movement desensitization: A case report' *Journal of Behaviour Therapy and Experimental Psychiatry* 1991 Vol. 22, pp.39–43.

6. Lipke, H. J., Botkin, A. L., 'Case studies of eye movement desensitization and reprocessing [EMDR] with chronic post-traumatic stress disorder', Veterans Affairs Medical Center, Psychology Service, North Chicago, Illinois, US *Psychotherapy* 1992 Win Vol. 29 (4), pp.591–5.

7. Kleinknecht, R. A., Morgan, M. P., 'Treatment of post-traumatic stress disorder with eye movement desensitization', Department of Psychology, Western Washington University, Bellingham 98225. *Journal of Behaviour Therapy and Experimental Psychiatry* (US) Mar 1992, 23 (1), pp.43–9.

CHAPTER 5

Emotions in the Eyes

The eyes indicate – more vividly, if not so precisely, than words or even intonations of the voice – our moods and emotions.
John Brophy, *The Human Race Reconsidered*

Have you ever noticed how difficult it is to be aware of what people are thinking or feeling when they wear sunglasses? This is because the eyes reveal more about our feelings and emotions than any other facial feature or combination of features. The eyes are by far the most powerful of communicators, expressing more about our true feelings even than the words we speak or the intonation of our voice. In fact, nothing portrays our true emotional states as accurately as the eyes. 'You cannot hide behind your eyes,' writes Lailan Young, author of the bestselling book *Secrets of the Face*,[1] 'only behind sunglasses.'

The explanation as to why the eyes are capable of revealing so much about our innermost feelings and emotions is found in the relationship between the eyes and the brain. The same portion of the brain that controls and monitors our emotions and feelings (the limbic system) also controls the eyes. Our moods and emotions therefore affect the function and appearance of the eyes and, conversely, our eyes can affect our emotional states.

The changes occur on a subconscious level. It is often completely involuntary; we do not realize that our eyes are giving away our secrets and it is very difficult and, in some cases, impossible, for us to consciously prevent them from so doing. Subtle changes occur simultaneously when we feel certain emotions which directly affect the movement and appearance of our eyes. Faces, it is said, can lie, but the eyes do not.

The pupils, for instance, change instantly in relation to our moods and emotions. Excitement and attraction make the pupils dilate, whereas anger, dislike and revulsion make the pupils contract. Some psychologists explain this phenomenon as the body's way of allowing us to experience more of those things that create happiness and reducing our experience of those things that cause stress and tension.

The response of the pupils therefore reveals a person's true feelings about any experience. If they don't like someone the pupils will contract, whereas if they do like someone, the pupils dilate. The next time you present a report to your boss, or ask someone how they like your new hairstyle or suit, or the next time you give someone a gift, if you want to know their true feelings, look closely at their pupils!

According to Dr Alexander Lowen MD, a prominent psychoanalyst and author of *The Language of the Body*,[2] 'The eyes transmit feeling more vividly than any spoken word. In my career as an analytic psychiatrist I have always relied upon the expression in the eyes of patients. I have seen their sadness and their fear, their rebuke and their anger; their appeal, their love and their hate.'[3]

Dr Lowen's views are supported by controlled clinical studies. A report in the *Journal of Nonverbal Behaviour*[4] cited the work of David Matsumoto at the Wright Institute, California, which examined the role of the eyes in expressing fear and anger. Using over 200 American and Japanese college students in three separate studies, Mr Matsumoto was left in no doubt that 'the eyes play an important role in labelling emotion and judging its intensity'.

Eye Contact – Self-Esteem and Depression

In October 1993, a report in the *American Journal of Psychology*[5] cited research undertaken at the Department of Psychology, Kings College, Pennsylvania. The researchers had demonstrated through a process of controlled interviews that a person's self-esteem could be evaluated through their eyes, or more specifically, through their eye contact during conversation. Eye contact, the report concluded, is a very powerful indicator of a person's feelings of self-worth. Firm eye contact was found to be an accurate indicator of a high self-esteem, whereas deliberate avoidance of eye contact was shown to be associated with a low self-esteem.

These findings were supported by a further study undertaken at the University of Bristol, UK,[6] which found that when people are suffering from clinical depression, they maintain much less eye contact than those who are not depressed. The researchers concluded that avoiding eye contact was probably part of an in-built defence mechanism through which a person could withdraw from reality. It is therefore apparent that when people shift their gaze rapidly during a conversation and refuse to maintain eye contact for any length of time, they are in effect saying that they do not feel good about themselves and they may also be suffering from depression.

The Emotions in a Gaze

> Every look reveals what is going on inside the mind of the person who gives it.
>
> A. J. Jackson

One look can say more than 1,000 words. It is a person's gaze – the direction and manner in which he or she looks – which reveals most about their emotions. In fact, so powerfully expressive is a gaze that many skilled parents and child minders rarely need raise their voice, let alone resort to violence, to convey their feelings to a child. Instead, they give the 'look' of disapproval and anger that will have an immediate effect on a child's behaviour.

Into adulthood and throughout our lives, most of the time our 'look' or gaze reflects our moods and feelings more expressively than any words we could muster. Psychologists agree that depression, anger, interest, boredom, fear or excitement are all revealed in varying intensities through a gaze. The more intense emotions are accompanied by a strong and more direct gaze.[7]

Depression

Clinical studies have shown that the body responds to depression in various ways; the shoulders slouch, breathing becomes shallow, facial muscles slacken, and the eyes avoid eye contact, shift frequently and mostly look downward. The body automatically takes on these characteristics when we feel depressed.

Interestingly, one of the quickest and easiest techniques to change a depressed state of mind is to consciously control our postures and eye movements. Pull the shoulders back, breathe deeply, smile, and look straight ahead or slightly upward. Even people who have suffered from manic depression and have been on medication for over 20 years cannot feel depressed whilst maintaining this posture and controlling their bodies in this way.

The eyelids also commonly flutter uncontrollably when we are feeling anxious, suffering from fatigue or feeling depressed. A full clinical evaluation of eyelid fluttering on 131 subjects revealed that it was also 'highly associated with endogenous depression and insomnia'.[8]

In severe, chronic depression, a distinctive fold appears in the upper eyelid. The fold (known as 'the Veraguth fold' after the researcher who identified it), seen in Figure 5.1, is

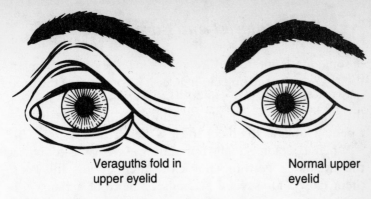

Veraguths fold in
upper eyelid

Normal upper
eyelid

*Figure 5.1 The Veraguth fold – a fold in the upper eyelid which
reveals severe, chronic depression.*

particularly noticeable in severely depressed patients over
30 years of age and is now a recognized retrospective, diagnostic sign of severe, chronic depression.[9]

Anger

Anger is easily detected in the eyes. If you think back to the
last big, confrontational argument you had, you will most
probably recall focusing your gaze directly and unflinch-
ingly on the other person's eyes, staring at them eyeball to
eyeball. This is an instinctive reaction when there is direct
conflict. But what you may not have noticed is that when
someone has done or said something that has made you
angry, the first thing you did was lower your eyebrows and
narrow your eyes almost as if squinting and, at the same
time, your pupils will have instantly contracted.

If you are one of those people who tends to avoid direct
conflicts, you would have avoided eye contact, and instead
looked sideways at the person out of the corner of your
eye, but you would still have lowered your eyebrows and
narrowed your eyes.

Interest and Boredom

If someone is interested in something, they will maintain their gaze upon the object for at least 33 per cent of the time when being shown it. The greater the interest, the greater the length of time they will gaze upon it. Conversely, the less a person looks at an object, the less they are interested in it.

When a person is really bored they use what is known as the 'eye-block' gesture. They close their eyelids and keep them closed for several seconds or more at a time. In a normal conversation, a person will blink six to eight times a minute, but when people are bored, they momentarily keep their eyes closed to 'block out' what they are hearing. Of course, in rare instances, this may only mean that the person is exhausted, but in such cases they will invariably nod off to sleep at some point!

Fear

When we experience fear, there are numerous reflexes that are triggered throughout the body. Our palms become moist with sweat, the complexion pales, and in extreme cases, the bowels move and the bladder empties! But fear, like other emotions, is first seen in the eyes which become wide-eyed and staring.

Exposed Eye Area and our Emotions

Researchers in India discovered that certain emotions can cause the eyes to widen or narrow. For instance, fear and surprise cause the eyes to widen and lengthen, exposing more of the eyes, whereas disgust has the reverse effect of narrowing the eyes.[10]

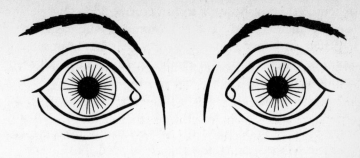

Figure 5.2: Wide-eyed and staring eyes – fear and surprise.

Figure 5.3: Narrowed eyes – anger and disgust.

Emotional Tendencies

Apart from showing emotions as and when they occur, the eyes also reveal our emotional tendencies. They tell us whether a person is more inclined to feelings of anxiety or anger, or whether he or she is easily upset or depressed.

The eyes may also show us why a person is inclined towards a specific emotion and how this can be changed.

How many times have you been amazed by what a close friend, work associate or even a family member has said or done? You thought you knew them – really knew them – and then they say or do something or react in such a way that you would never have expected from them. The truth is, of course, that we rarely understand people, let alone know them, even those closest to us.

Yet we all have different emotional tendencies, a genetic

or acquired predisposition to certain emotions. One person is easily angered and has a short temper, whereas another is placid and easy-going. One person is easily upset and anxious, while another is rarely riled. We all display our emotions differently and even identical twins rarely share exactly the same emotional disposition. We can spend years of our lives with someone and never really know them and yet, when we understand the secrets in the eyes, we can accurately assess someone's emotional predispositions.

Figure 5.4a: Long, thick eyelashes – a highly emotional disposition.

Figure 5.4b: Fine eyelashes – a cool and detached personality.

Eyelashes

The eyelashes are considered by Siang Mien masters to be strong indicators of our emotions. For instance, long, thick eyelashes are said to indicate that a person is very emotional; fine eyelashes on the other hand suggest a cool, detached person, and eyelashes that curl are a signal of an optimistic or passionate nature.

Figure 5.4c: Curled eyelashes – an optimistic and passionate nature.

The General Appearance of the Eyes

According to the science of Siang Mien, the general appearance of the eyes reveals a lot about a person's emotional tendencies. Deep-set eyes as in Figure 5.5 denote a

Figure 5.5: Deep-set eyes.

withdrawn, secretive person. Close-set eyes are said to belong to people who are reserved and conscious of their appearance. Large eyes are associated with impulsive and passionate people, whereas small eyes indicate a person who is often secretive and reserved.

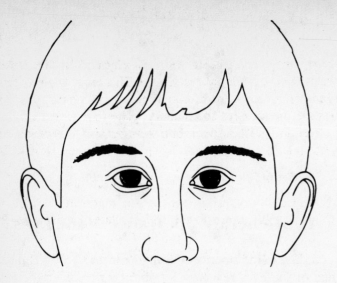

Figure 5.6: Close-set eyes.

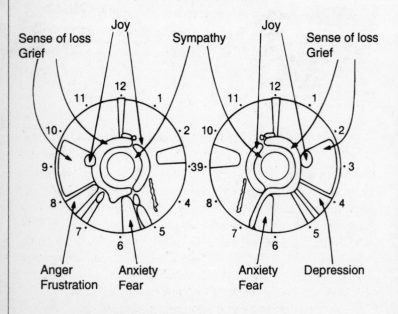

Figure 5.7: Emotional tendencies in the iris.

Iris Markings

Whilst a person's iris shows their physical health, it also reveals their emotional tendencies. This is because certain organs affect and are affected by specific emotions. For instance, the kidneys and bladder relate to fear and anxiety, the liver and gall bladder relate to anger and frustration, the lungs and colon to grief and loss, the spleen and stomach to depression, and the heart and small intestines relate to joy.

Figure 5.7 shows the location of emotional tendencies in the iris. Each area represents specific emotions to which a person will be predisposed. These relate precisely to the teachings in the *Nei De Ching* (*The Chinese Book of Medicine*, reputedly 4,000 years old), and I have found them to be extremely accurate in my clinical observations.

When, for instance, there is a discolouration in the kidney region of someone's iris, that person will be predisposed to feelings of fear and anxiety. On the other hand, if there is a discolouration in the liver region, the person will be short-tempered and predisposed to anger.

Changing Moods through the Eyes

Emotions and moods affect the eyes but they are also affected by the eyes. It was not until 1942 that evidence began to emerge that different colours could, when viewed, influence our nervous system and our moods. A Russian scientist, S. V. Krakov, discovered that red and blue had contrasting effects on the sympathetic and parasympathetic nervous systems.[11] His findings were later confirmed in 1958 by Robert Gerard who, as part of his doctorate dissertation in psychology, conducted experiments to evaluate the psychological and physiological effects on the human body of viewing coloured lights.[12]

Mr Gerard's research was designed specifically to discover whether viewing different colours arouses different feelings and emotions. The experiment was simple: red, blue and white lights of equal intensity and brightness were projected at different times onto a screen viewed by 24 men. The red light was found to increase the viewers' blood pressure, respiratory movements, arousal via palmar conductance (sweaty palms) and eye-blink frequency. The viewers also reported feeling tense, anxious and excited. Yet, when the blue and white lights were viewed, all the physiological factors decreased and the viewers reported feeling calmer and more relaxed.

These findings were supported during the same year by

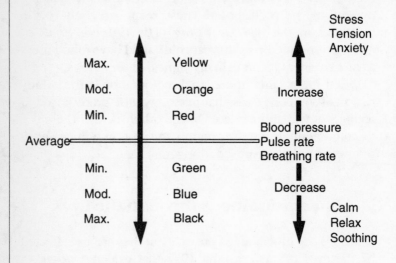

Figure 5.8: How colours affect our moods.

experiments carried out by Dr Harry Wohlfarth who found that blood pressure, pulse rate and respiration rates were increased when people are in red surroundings, but that yellow and orange had even greater stimulatory effects. Dr Wohlfarth found that blue reduced these effects by calming the nervous system, as did green (to a lesser degree) and black (to a greater degree).[13]

Later studies[14] added further weight to the growing

evidence that specific colours, when viewed, affect our moods, blood pressure, pulse rate and breathing patterns. Red, orange and yellow are, in effect, visual stimulants, whereas green, blue and black are calmatives.

Seasonal Affective Disorder and the eyes

Seasonal Affective Disorder (SAD) is the term used to describe a depressive state brought about through inadequate exposure to daylight. However, it is not exposure of the *skin* to daylight which is the main determining factor, but rather exposure of the *eyes* to the light.

Recent research[15] has established that depressed patients suffering from SAD respond well to treatment with bright artificial light (phototherapy), but the beneficial effects are greatly enhanced if the light is shone on the eyes rather than on the skin. The researchers concluded that it is the amount and quality of light received by the eyes that determines our susceptibility to SAD and that light, when received by the eyes, has antidepressant effects which enables patients to overcome this disorder.

Endnotes

1. Young, L., *Secrets of the Face*, p.89, Coronet, 1983.
2. Collier MacMillan Publishers, 1958.
3. *The Language of the Body*, p.366.
4. 'Face, culture, and judgments of anger and fear: Do the eyes have it?' Matsumoto, David Wright Inst, Berkeley, California, *US Journal of Nonverbal Behavior* 1989 Fal Vol. 13 (3), pp.171–88.
5. Droney, J. M., Brooks, C. I., 'Attributions of self-esteem as a function of duration of eye contact' Department of Psychology, King's College, Wilkes-Barre, Pennsylvania 18711, *Journal of Social Psychology* (US) Oct 1993, 133 (5), pp.715–22.
6. Hinchliffe, M. K., Lancashire, M., Roberts, F. J. U., 'A study of eye-

contact changes in depressed and recovered psychiatric patients', Bristol, England, *British Journal of Psychiatry* Aug 1971, Vol. 119 (549), pp.213–15.

7. Kimble, C. E., Olszewski, D. A.,'Gaze and emotional expression: The effects of message positivity-negativity and emotional intensity', *Journal of Research in Personality* Mar 1980, Vol. 14 (1), pp.60–9.

8. Schwarz, L. H., Stern, J.A.,'Eyelid tremulousness:A neurophysiological index of depression', 1420 Grattan Street, Saint Louis, Missourri, *Archives of General Psychiatry* 1968, 19 (4), pp.497–500.

9. Meyer, R. B. U., 'Diagnostic significance of the so-called Veraguth upper eyelid folds in depressed patients', Basel, Ophthalmologic Clinic, Switzerland, *Schweizer Archiv für Neurologie, Neurochirurgie und Psychiatrie* 1970, Vol. 107 (2), pp.347–62.

10. Mandal, M. K., Pandey, R., Madan, S. K., Banaras, 'Exposed eye area (EEA) in the expression of various emotions', Hindu University, Varanasi, India, *Journal of General Psychology* Oct 1992, Vol. 119 (4), pp.385–9.

11. Krakov, S. V., 'Colour vision and autonomic nervous system' *Journal of Optical Society of America*, June 1942.

12. Gerard, R. M., 'Differential effects of coloured lights on psychophysiological functions', PhD diss, University of California, 1958.

13. Wohlfarth, H., 'Psychological evaluation of experiments to assert the effects of colour-stimuli upon the autonomic nervous system' *Exerpta Medica, Neurology and Psychiatry*, 2, No. 4, 1958.

14. Aaronson, B. S., 'Colour perception and affect' *American Journal of Clinical Hypnosis* 14 (1971), pp.38–42.

15. Plack, J. J., and Schick, J.,'The effects of colour on human behaviour' *Journal of the Association for Study in Perception* 9 (1974), pp.4–16.

16. Wehr, T. A., Skwerer, R. G., Jacobsen, F. M., Sack, D. A. et al, 'Eye versus skin phototherapy of seasonal affective disorder', NIMH, Bethesda, MD *American Journal of Psychiatry* Jun 1987, Vol. 144 (6), pp.753–7.

CHAPTER 6

Character and Personality in the Eyes

The countenance is the portrait of the mind,
the eyes its informers.
Cicero, Rome's famed orator

It was once said that every man has three characters – that which he exhibits, that which he thinks he has, and that which he has.[1] Character is the sum of the qualities that make one person different to any other. It is character that 'maketh the man' because it is character that determines how a person will react to any given set of circumstances; 'Character,' wrote the Greek philosopher Heraclitis, 'is destiny.'

It is not easy to understand a person's true character because we tend to judge people from what they exhibit – their words and deeds. This is presumably what led one cynic, Mercelene Cox, to write: 'No man knows his true character until he has run out of gas, purchased something on an instalment plan and raised an adolescent!' We can't see inside someone's head, or understand their feelings, their motives or their inner qualities. Or can we?

Physiognomists have been saying for thousands of years that certain facial features reveal a great deal about a person's character. The physiognomists contend that in our faces are written the qualities of our characters, and all physiognomists agree that of all the features of the face, the most important one in determining a man's character is his eyes. When we study the expression of the face as a measure of character and of the personality,' wrote Dr Alexander Lowen MD, 'our attention should be directed first to the eyes.'[2]

One of the most celebrated European physiognomists was a Swiss pastor and teacher by the name of Johann Casper Lavater who lived in the eighteenth century. During his life, Lavater was reputed to be able to read a man's character from his silhouette. His book, *Essays on Physiognomy*, published in 1775, became a bestseller and was translated into many different languages. But, even 'for Lavater,' wrote John Liggett, senior lecture in Psychology at University College Cardiff at the University of Wales, 'the eyes were the most powerful of all signals of character.'[3] 'Well-defined eye bones and easily delineated firm arches,' wrote Lavater, 'I never saw but in noble and great men.'

This may, at first, seem too fantastical to be given any credence but, in recent years, psychologists have discovered that the eyes are indeed very closely related to our character and personality. The results of numerous research projects have revealed that the eyes are powerful indicators of personality and character disorders. For instance, rapid vertical eye movements are related to anxiety,[4] and schizophrenia,[5] whereas rapid horizontal eye movements are associated with alexithymia (inability to understand the printed or written word).[6]

There have also been a number of studies demonstrating the relationship between the movement and gaze of the eyes in schizophrenia.[7] Dr Alexander Lowen MD, psychoanalyst and author, states:

It is in his eyes that the schizophrenic shows most clearly his illness. One can make the diagnosis, at times, from the eyes alone ... They seem to look through you and not at you. When you look at their eyes you feel that you do not make contact with them.[8]

Intelligence and the Eye

The renowned Greek philosopher, scientist and teacher, Pythagoras, was reputed to assess his prospective students' intelligence from their eyes and it is reported that he would refuse to accept students if their eyes did not indicate that they were sufficiently cerebrally gifted to fully benefit from his tuition. Whilst Pythagoras' actions may, at first consideration, appear bizarre, researchers have demonstrated that intelligence and academic ability are very closely related to the eyes and can even be assessed to a limited degree by the eyes.

For instance, there is a definite correlation between intelligence and myopia (short-sightedness).[9] Researchers at the School of Optometry attached to the University of Waterloo, Ontario, Canada confirmed this finding. The researchers studied over 700 European and Maori children and found that there was a significantly higher level of intelligence among myopic (short-sighted) individuals than hypermetropic (long-sighted) children.[10]

Whilst, at first sight, it may seem strange that short-sighted children should tend to be more intelligent than long-sighted children, the researchers put forward several logical explanations for their findings. One suggestion was that myopia is regarded as an overdevelopment of the eye, just as hypermetropia (long-sightedness) is seen as underdevelopment, and therefore the eye may simply mirror the development of the brain. The logic behind this theory being that large-brained people are generally considered to be more intelligent than smaller-brained people.

Another hypothesis which was put forward to explain the fact that myopic children tend to be more intelligent than other children is simply that intelligent children tend to read more, and long hours of study are often a causative or contributory factor leading to short-sightedness.

Another sign of intelligence or lack of intelligence from which people intuitively make judgements about a person's intelligence lies in eye contact during a conversation. Researchers at Southwest Texas State University[11] demonstrated that the duration of eye contact and the frequency with which a person shifted his gaze is considered by interviewers to be a reliable indicator of a person's intelligence. Poor eye contact and frequent shifts in gaze were considered to be reflective of a lower intelligence, whilst maintaining firm eye contact was considered to be a sign of a higher intelligence. (It should be noted, however, that low self-esteem, dishonesty and depressive states may also be factors causing a person to avoid eye contact).

The Field of Vision and Learning Disabilities

What you are able to perceive around you while looking straight ahead is known as your field of vision. When you are driving down a narrow street behind a very slow driver, the chances are that he/she has an impaired visual field. These people are hazards to themselves and everyone else and, without doubt, they can inadvertently 'cause' accidents because they cannot see things until they are straight in front of them. Whilst looking straight ahead at the road, they cannot 'see' what is going on around them. Pedestrians or other cars 'appear from nowhere' because the driver is not able to see them until they are within their field of vision.

Whilst, in physical terms, the field of vision represents how much of the world our brains are able to perceive visually, according to Professor Jacob Libermann, a leading researcher in light and vision, the visual field also represents how much of the brain is actually functioning.[12] The smaller the field, the less the brain is functioning and, conversely, the greater the field of vision, the more the brain is functioning.

One area where this theory has been proven is in a person's learning skills. In 1957, a report published in the American Journal of Ophthalmology revealed that children with learning disabilities consistently had smaller visual fields than children without learning disabilities. Dr Thomas Eames, a physician at Boston University, found that eight out of ten children who had constricted fields of vision were failing in school work in one or more subjects. The essence of Dr Eames' work was that there was indeed a direct causal relationship between one's fields of vision and learning skills.

You can test your field of vision very simply by covering one eye and focusing the other eye on an object about 20 inches in front of you. Hold your arms out by your sides and level with your shoulders as in Figure 6.1 and slowly draw your arms together until you notice when each arm comes into your field of vision. Repeat the same test using the other eye and this then reveals your horizontal field of vision – how much you can see around you.

A similar test can be done to establish your vertical field of vision. In this case, hold your arm above your head and, looking straight ahead with the corresponding eye, but keeping the other eye closed, bring down the arm until you are aware of your thumb. Then do the same, this time holding your arm by your side and raising it until you become aware of your thumb. Then simply repeat the process on the other side and you will then have a fairly good assessment of your vertical field of vision – what can be seen above and below you.

A normal horizontal field of vision should be almost 180 degrees and the vertical field of vision should be approximately 120 degrees. If your field of vision is significantly less than these figures, it would be a good idea to consult your optometrist for a detailed examination. Not only will corrective measures help you to see more (and therefore be a safer driver), but it may also help improve your learning skills. This is, of course, particularly relevant to schoolchildren and students with learning difficulties. An effective remedial treatment is syntronics (light therapy) and many case histories are detailed in Professor Libermann's book *Light: The Medicine of the Future*.[13]

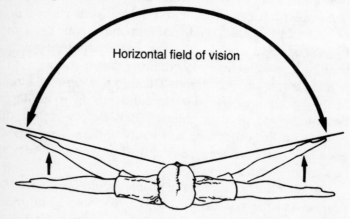

(a) Testing vertical field of vision

Vertical field of vision

(b) Testing horizontal field of vision

Horizontal field of vision

Figure 6.1: Testing your field of vision.

Strong Eyebrows – Power and Authority

In both Eastern and European physiognomy, the eyebrows are considered to be indications of a person's moral and personal characteristics. Strong eyebrows are said to reveal authority and power as well as virility. Lavater wrote: 'I never yet saw a profound thinker or a man of fortitude and prudence with weak, high eyebrows.' By weak eyebrows, he was referring not to their size, but to the sparseness of the hair. Conversely, a 'strong' eyebrow meant thick, dense eyebrow hairs.

High eyebrows are those which appear to be some distance from the eye itself. This is not a good sign as it is said to indicate a person whose ambitions exceed their capabilities. Such people are considered to lack patience and can consequently be short tempered.

Lavater also stated that the closer together the eyebrows, the more earnest and firm the character. When these are seen, the person is usually more resolute and firm in decision, refusing to procrastinate or vacillate. On the other hand, the more remote the eyebrows are from each other, the more the character becomes volatile and easily moved and persuaded.

Figure 6.2: Eyebrows close to the eyes – autocratic, self-reliant character.

When you look at political leaders, and especially autocrats past and present, you will find that they all share at least one characteristic – strong eyebrows which are very close to the eyes. In autocratic despots the eyebrows are so close to the eyes that they appear to be pressing on top of the eyes. Interestingly, other physiognomists came independently to the same conclusion. Giovanni Battista Della Porta wrote that strong eyebrows reveal power and the sixteenth-century physiognomist Thomas Hill wrote: 'A brow in length indicates good sense.' Avicenna, the Arab philosopher and physician, concluded that well-developed eyebrows were also the sign of power with a tendency to guile. The Siang Mien masters in China also concurred with this finding. To them, thick, strong eyebrows belong to a person with a strong personality with leadership qualities.

The Siang Mien masters scrupulously analysed their subjects' eyebrows and, like their European counterparts, found that specific characteristics could be seen in different types of eyebrows.

Figure 63a: The ideal eyebrow.

1. The Ideal Eyebrow

The ideal eyebrow is a strong eyebrow, longer at both ends than the eye and rounded at the medial end whilst tapering away to a point at the lateral end. It is an index finger width away from the eye itself and is filled with shining, lustrous hairs.

2. Broom Eyebrows

Where the eyebrows scatter at either end, they are referred to as 'brooms'. People with these eyebrows are said to often lack sufficient drive and motivation to see a project through from beginning to end. If the eyebrows scatter at the lateral ends (brooms up), it suggests that these people are best in

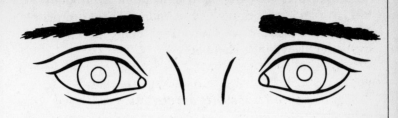

Figure 6.3bi: Broom eyebrows up.

Figure 6.3bii: Broom eyebrows down.

initiating a project, whereas if the eyebrows are scattered at the medial end (brooms down), the person is said to be better in the final stages of a project.

3. Hero Eyebrows

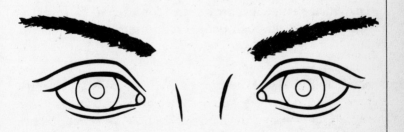

Figure 6.3c: Hero eyebrows.

Hero eyebrows are particularly long, point slightly upward and have an ideal beginning and ending. These are people whose thoughts are well organized, energetic, ambitious and generally willing to help others.

4. Chaotic Eyebrows

Figure 6.3d: Chaotic eyebrows.

As their name suggests, chaotic eyebrows have hairs which seem to point in all directions. These are said to belong to people who do not organize their thoughts well and have difficulties maintaining concentration for long periods of time.

5. Triangle Eyebrows

Triangular-shaped eyebrows are considered to reveal a selfish nature although people with them are also said to

Figure 6.3e: Triangle eyebrows.

possess great courage. If triangle eyebrows have elongated lateral ends, it is said to indicate a clever but often cruel personality.

7. New Moon Eyebrows

Figure 6.3f: New moon eyebrows.

New moon eyebrows are thin semi-circles and reveal an emotional and passionate person who, it is said, possesses strong sex drives.

8. Character Eight Eyebrows

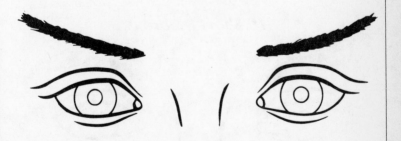

Figure 6.3g: Character eight eyebrows.

Character eight eyebrows are so called because they resemble the Chinese character for the number eight. People with these eyebrows are not thought to be good leaders and are therefore considered to be better suited as employees than employers.

9. Vertical Hairs at the Medial End of the Eyebrows

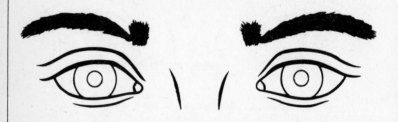

Figure 6.3h: Vertical hairs at the medial end of the eyebrows.

The masters of Siang Mien believed that where the hairs at the medial end of the eyebrow are seen to grow vertically, it indicates that the person has brothers, sisters or family relatives who are not particularly kind or helpful.

10. Short Eyebrows

Figure 6.3i: Short eyebrows.

If the eyebrows are shorter in length than the eye itself, they are said to reveal a selfishness, an impatient nature and a short temper.

11. One Eyebrow Higher than the Other

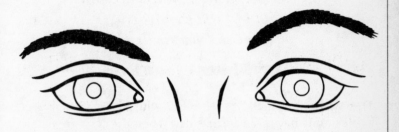

Figure 6.3j: One eyebrow higher than the other.

If one eyebrow appears higher than the other, it is said to indicate a moody personality, liable to swift mood swings.

Large and Small Eyes

In China, Siang Mien masters consider large eyes to be associated with impulsive and passionate people. They are also open, honest people and find it difficult keeping a secret. If you want to keep a secret, warn the masters of Siang Mien, do not tell it to a person with large eyes. Small eyes, on the other hand, are said to reveal a more reserved, cautious nature.

Pointed Inner Tips

According to the Siang Mien masters, if a person's eyes have pointed inner tips, they tend to lack concentration and consequently they are not considered to be particularly adept at mentally demanding jobs.

Figure 6.3k: Pointed inner tips.

The Whites of the Eyes

The whites of the eyes should (with the exception of babies) only be visible at the sides. When the sclera is visible either above or below the iris, the Siang Mien masters warn of a hypersensitive, self-centred person. If the whites are seen above the iris as in Figure 6.4b, it is said to reveal a person who is easily offended and who has a cruel streak.

All those people whose eyes show the whites visible either above or below the iris are said by the Chinese to be accident prone with a need to take especial care of their health.

Figure 6.4a: Two whites – either side of the iris.

Figure 6.4b: Three whites – extra white seen above the iris.

Figure 6.4c: Three whites – extra white seen below the iris.

The General Shape of the Eye and the Eight Character Types

All physiognomists believe the general shape of the eye to be very important in understanding a person's character and personality. The Siang Mien masters wrote of eight different categories of eye shapes, all of which indicate aspects of a person's character.

The Dragon

Figure 6.5: The shapes of the eyes.

(a) The Dragon.

In Chinese culture, the dragon is a symbol of power and authority. Not surprisingly then, people with dragon eyes are believed to have a strong personality, and to be brave and courageous. The owners of dragon eyes are said to be very creative people. They tend to be sociable, personable and often very generous by nature. Dragon eyes are large,

99

elongated and almond-shaped with large areas of white to the left and right of the iris.

The Cow

(b) The Cow.

The cow eye is less elongated than the dragon and therefore appears large and suggests an open, frank and direct manner. People with this eye shape are said to be trustworthy and honest, although if the eye is very large, they may find it difficult keeping a secret.

The Peacock

(c) The Peacock.

The peacock eye is slightly upward slanting and appears almost rectangular in shape. It reveals an emotional person whose actions and decisions are often driven by feelings and emotions rather than objective reasoning. When peacock eyes are narrowed with smaller areas of whites on either side of the iris there is said to be a tendency to excessive jealousy which needs to be controlled.

The Tiger and the Fox

(d) The Tiger.

(e) The Fox.

The tiger eye is an oval-shaped eye and represents a person who is persistent, rational and forward thinking. However, when the eye narrows, it becomes known as a fox shape, which is a sign of cunning. The Siang Mien masters recommend exercising caution when doing business dealings with fox-eyed people.

The Triangle and the Chicken

(f) The Triangle.

101

(g) The Chicken.

A large triangular eye suggests an authoritarian and manipulative nature. Triangular-eyed people do not stand for any criticism or disagreement. It should not come as a surprise, then, that people with this eye are, say the Chinese, particularly suited for a political career.

If the triangular eye has an upper eyelid that droops, it is known as a chicken. Chicken-eyed people are considered by Siang Mien masters to be interfering busybodies with a nervous disposition, who spend their time fretting and rushing about like a clucking chicken.

The New Moon

(h) The New Moon.

An eye shaped like a new moon is said to indicate a tendency to dishonesty and cunning, greater even than the fox eye. People are warned by the Siang Mien masters to tread very carefully when dealing with a person who has new moon eyes.

The Iris and your Character

The coloured part of the eye known as the iris has always been referred to as an indicator of a person's character. Reading a person's character from the colour of their eyes was, for instance, particularly popular during Elizabethan times when a grey eye was considered to reflect a sly nature, a brown eye a roguish and mysterious nature, and a green eye revealed a jealous disposition.

More reliable and accurate, though no less remarkable, are the findings of researchers at the University of California who recently discovered that there is a strong correlation between eye colour and our behaviour patterns. Psychologists had suspected for some time that our eye colouring was, in some way, connected to inhibition. The researchers put this assumption to the test by selecting two-year-old children on the basis of eye colour only – brown and blue – and observing their behaviour. The researchers found that there was a 'significant association between blue-eyed children and behavioural inhibition', whereas brown-eyed infants were more likely to be uninhibited.[14]

Iris Structure and Personality

As discussed in Chapter 3, clinical iridologists have observed that the fibres in the iris reveal a lot about a person's nervous disposition and indicate whether a person finds it difficult to relax and unwind or to have a more laid-back approach to life.

The Rayid Interpretation of Irises – Character and Personality

The Rayid system of analysing irises concentrates on the relationships between markings in the iris and our personality and character. Mr Denny Johnson, pioneer of this new science, teaches how three distinct personality types can be spotted from four different iris types referred to as jewels, flowers, streams and shakers.

The Jewel Iris

The jewel iris is characterized by pigments (known by traditional iridologists as 'psora') which look like jewels dotted around the iris. People with a jewel iris are said to be intellectual and analytical by nature as well as perceptive and inquisitive. 'Jewels' have strong verbal communicators which, coupled with their analytical minds, make them excellent orators and therefore leaders. Apparently, only 15 per cent of the population in the United States has a pure jewel-type iris.

(a) The jewel iris.

The Flower Iris

The flower iris contains open fibres (referred to by traditional iridologists as a 'net' structure), giving the appearance of an open flower. Flower irises are said to reveal an emotional and often spontaneous character with strong creative skills. People with flower irises, therefore, often become artists, entertainers, writers and actors. Approximately 20 per cent of the United States population has pure flower irises.

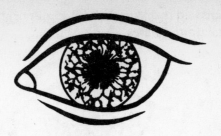

(b) The flower iris.

The Stream Iris

The stream iris has fibres that appear as streaks. People with this iris tend to be very sensitive, physically and emotionally. They are said to have strong intuitive and empathetic skills and therefore often find themselves in service or caring professions. About 30 per cent of the population in the United States are said to have a pure stream iris.

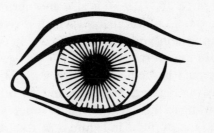

(c) The stream iris

The Shaker Iris

The shaker iris is a combination of a jewel and a flower iris. These are people who are often intense, tenacious and zealous – the requirement of pioneers. These people can achieve the heights of success or the depths of failure. They prefer to break new ground rather than following in the footsteps of others and consequently are inclined towards pioneering roles – inventors, explorers or motivators. Pure

105

shakers are said to make up about 15 per cent of the population of the United States.

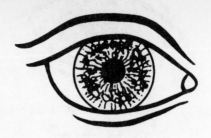

(d) The shaker iris.

Extroversion and Introversion

We have already discovered that, at least in infancy, brown-eyed people tend to be less inhibited than people with blue eyes *(see page 103)*. There is also another method used in the Rayid system of iris analysis which is referred to as 'the ring of expression' and is said to reveal whether someone is extrovert or introvert.

In a normal iris, the nerve wreath should be about a third of the way out between the pupil and the outer edge of the iris. According to the Rayid system of iridology, if the wreath is closer to the pupil, as in Figure 6.7a, the person will tend to be introverted, whereas if it is further away from the pupil, as in Figure 6.7b, the person will be more extroverted. There may well be some truth in this finding as a nerve wreath which is close to the pupil also reveals a tense colon and therefore a tendency to constipation *(see Chapter 3)*. People who suffer with constipation are believed to 'hold things in' emotionally, unable to express their innermost fears and emotions. Naturally, they will therefore tend to be introverted.

Figure 6.7a: Wreath close to pupil – introversion.

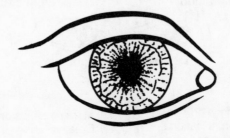

Figure 6.7b: Wreath away from pupil – extroversion.

Right and Left-Brained People

It is now well accepted by clinical psychologists that the right and left hemispheres of the brain control different physiological and psychological functions. The right side of the brain is involved with more emotional or spiritual pursuits, the left with practical, analytical endeavours.

We all tend to be dominant in one or other side of the brain; right-brained people (i.e. those who predominantly use the right side of the brain) are creative and imaginative. They tend to sleep on their left side with their left cheek down, sit with the left leg over the right, and stand leaning on the left leg. They also tend, for some as yet unknown reason, to look like the father's side of the family.

Left-brained people are the exact opposite; they are stronger in organizational, administrative and planning skills, sleep on their right side, sit with the right leg over the

107

left, stand leaning to the right and tend to look like their mother's side of the family.

We can assess whether a person is left or right-brained by observing their eyes. If there are more noticeable markings in the left eye, the person is right-brained and vice versa. This is because the right eye is controlled by the left side of the brain and the left eye is controlled by the right side of the brain.

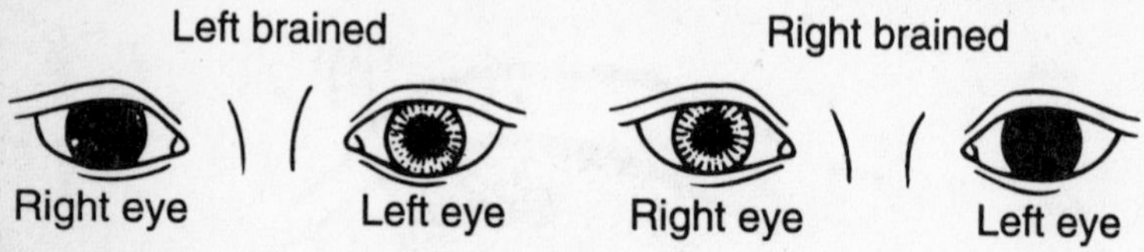

Left brained   Right brained

Right eye   Left eye   Right eye   Left eye

- More markings on *right* iris
- Strong in organisational, administrative and planning skills
- Tend to look like mother's side of the family
- Sleeps on right side
- Stand predominantly on *right* leg
- Better rapport with father

- More markings on *left* iris
- Creative, imaginative Tends to look like father's side of the family
- Sleeps on left side
- Stands predominantly on *left* leg
- Better rapport with mother

Figure 6.8: Right and left-brained people revealed in the irises.

Eye Movements and Character

The direction in which a person tends to move his or her eyes during a conversation is also believed to reveal details about their character. It is accepted that our eye movements are influenced by our thought processes (*see Chapter* 7) and researchers have demonstrated that the general direction of our eye movements during a conversation also reveals whether we tend to be emotional and moved by feelings or assertive and practical. For instance, one study involving 89 college students found that there was a significant correlation to suggest that people who tend to look more to the left during a conversation are more assertive, shrewd and suspicious by nature than those who look to the right, and that those people who tend to look to the right in preference to the left during a conversation are, it seems, more emotional, sensitive individuals.[14]

Endnotes

1. Alphonse Karr, 1808-90.
2. *The Language of the Body,* p.105, Collier Macmillan Publishers, 1958.
3. Liggett, J., *The Human Face,* Constable & Co, 1974.
4. Lund, H. G., Bech, P., Eplov, L., Jennum, P., Wildschiodtz, G., 'An epidemiological study of REM latency and psychiatric disorders.' Department of Psychiatry, Rigshospitalet, Copenhagen, Denmark, *Journal of Affective Disorders* (Netherlands) Nov 1991, 23 (3), pp.107-12.
5. Lencz, T., Raine, A., Scerbo, A., Redmon, M., Brodish, S., Holt, L., Bird, L., 'Impaired eye tracking in undergraduates with schizotypal personality disorder', Department of Psychology, University of Southern California, Los Angeles 90089-1061, *American Journal of Psychiatry* (US) Jan 1993, 150 (1), pp.152-4.
6. Siever, L. J., Keefe, R., Bernstein, D. P., Coccaro, E. F., Klar, H. M., Zemishlany, Z., Peterson, A. E., Davidson, M., Mahon, T., Horvath, T. et al., 'Eye tracking impairment in clinically identified patients with schizotypal personality disorder' Department of Psychiatry, Mount Sinai School of Medicine, Bronx, NY, *American Journal of Psychiatry* (US) Jun 1990, 147 (6), pp.740-5.
7. Parker, J. D., Taylor, G. J., Bagby, R. M., 'Relationship between conjugate lateral eye movements and alexithymia', Department of Psychology, York University, Toronto, Canada, *Psychotherapy and Psychosomatics* (Switzerland) 1992, 57 (3), pp.94-101.

8. Ibid (5).
9. *The Language of the Body,* p.366.
10. Miller, E. M., 'On the correlation of myopia and intelligence', University of New Orleans, LA, US *Genetic, Social and General Psychology Monographs* 1992 Nov Vol. 118 (4), pp.361-83.
11. Grosvenor, T., 'Refractive state, intelligence test scores, and academic ability. University of Waterloo, School of Optometry, Ontario, Canada, *American Journal of Optometry* and Archives of American Academy of Optometry 1970, May Vol. 47 (5), pp.355-61.
12. Wheeler, R. W., Baron, J. C., Michell, S., Ginsburg, H. J., 'Eye contact and the perception of intelligence', *Southwest Texas State University Bulletin of the Psychonomic Society* 1979 Feb Vol. 13 (2), pp.101-2.
13. *Light: Medicine of the Future,* p.82, Bear & Co, 1991.
14. Rosenberg, A. A., Kagan, J., 'Physical and physiological correlates of behavioral inhibition', University of California, Berkeley 94708, *Developmental Psychobiology* (US) Dec 1989, 22 (8), pp.753-70.
15. Etaugh, C. F., Bradley, U., 'Personality correlates of lateral eye movement and handedness', *Perceptual and Motor Skills* Jun 1972, Vol 34 (3), pp.751-4.

CHAPTER 7

Thoughts in the Eyes

The eyes of a man converse as much as the tongue, with the
advantage that the ocular dialect needs no dictionary, but is
understood the world over.
Ralph Waldo Emerson

It is widely accepted that our facial expressions can reveal
our innermost thoughts and emotions. A beaming smile
may show happiness and joy, and a frown, sadness. But facial
expressions can lie - people can put on 'brave faces' and
they can cry 'crocodile tears' - and sometimes they can lie
so well that it is difficult to be sure of a person's true
thoughts and feelings.

Yet there remains one facial signal which psychologists
have found cannot be controlled and therefore can never lie
- and that signal is in the eyes. In fact, according to John
Brophy, physiognomist and author of *The Human Face
Reconsidered*, the eye is so expressive of our thoughts that
the only way to be certain of concealing your thoughts from
others is to 'lower the upper eyelids until very little of the
eye is showing'.[1]

The Pupil – Likes, Dislikes and Excitement

The pupil is the black circle in the middle of your eye. Its
size is controlled by the iris. In bright sunlight, the pupil

contracts, preventing too much light entering the eye which would otherwise damage the retina. In a dimly-lit room, the pupils dilate allowing more light into the eyes so that you may see more clearly. But the pupil does not only respond to light, it is also controlled by our thoughts and emotions.

Likes and Dislikes

Two and a half thousand years ago, Confucius wrote: 'Look into a person's pupils. He cannot hide himself.' Today, researchers have confirmed that the pupils do in fact reveal our innermost thoughts and cannot be consciously controlled. For instance, if you look at something that you like, your pupils will immediately dilate, sometimes by three or four times. The greater the appeal, the larger the dilation. Conversely, if you see something that you dislike, your pupils will contract in size, and the more you dislike the object, the smaller your pupils will contract.

In the past 25 years there has been a great deal of research into the response of the pupils to our thoughts which has produced very interesting results. Studies were undertaken in controlled laboratory conditions, taking care to ensure that the light on each subject was constant so that the researchers could be certain that any pupil distortions would be due solely to the subject's thoughts and feelings.

Looking at Babies

In one experiment, photographs of human babies were shown to single men and women, married men and women who were at the time childless and married couples who had children. All of the women had strong pupil dilations, regardless of whether they were single, married and childless, or married with children.

The men, on the other hand, who were single or married

without any children showed pupil constrictions, whereas only those men who were fathers showed strong pupil dilations. Therefore, psychologists conclude, whilst all women seem to have a maternal instinct, men do not tend to acquire a real interest in babies or a paternal instinct until they have fathered their own child.[2]

Fibbing about Foods

In another experiment, people were shown different foods and asked if they liked them. As you might expect, in most cases the pupil response matched exactly the person's declared preferences. The more they said they liked the food, the greater the dilation of the pupil and conversely, the less they liked the food the more the pupil contracted. The researchers were intrigued as to why there had been a discrepancy in a few individuals between what they said they liked and the way in which their pupils responded, but when the researchers questioned those individuals further, the answer became clear. Those few people had 'fibbed' about their dietary preferences because they were on strict weight-loss diets but they still secretly longed for the 'forbidden' foods!

Excitement

The pupils also dilate when we feel excited. The greater the excitement, the larger the pupils dilate. It is for this reason that the ancient Chinese jade traders watched their buyers' pupils closely when negotiating prices. Dilated pupils were a sure signal of the buyer's interest and indicated that the price was still too low. The famous anthropologist and author, Desmond Morris, explains that the jade dealers 'took to wearing dark glasses expressly in order to conceal their excited pupil dilations when they handled a particularly valuable specimen of jade'.[3]

Pupilliary reactions are heavily relied upon by professional gamblers. Experiments carried out with expert poker players revealed that their success rate fell dramatically when their opponents wore dark glasses. This was because the pupil signals which had previously revealed the strength of their opponents' hands and therefore whether or not they were bluffing were no longer visible and, as a result, the experts won far fewer games.[4]

It is therefore quite easy to find out whether or not someone likes or is really excited by what he or she is being shown or told. All you need do is simply watch the reaction of their pupils. The bigger the pupils become, the more they like what they see, the smaller the pupils become, the less they like it. And if you play poker, don't bet on a hand if another player's pupils become noticeably dilated!

Understanding People's Thought Processes

Have you ever noticed, when talking to people, how their eyes move in different directions? One minute they're looking you in the eye, when suddenly they look upwards to the right or downwards to the left. Have you ever wondered why they do this or what it means?

The direction in which we move our eyes reveals the nature of our thoughts. If the eyes are the windows of the soul, the way we move our eyes is the gateway to our mind. This is because the nerves that control our eye movements work very closely with the part of the brain known as the limbic system which responds to our sensory stimuli – sight, sound, smell, taste and touch. Consequently, the direction in which we move our eyes often accurately reveals what is going on inside our minds.

Researchers of the relatively new science of Neuro-Linguistic Programming (NLP) have discovered through controlled studies that the way we move our eyes is determined by what thoughts we are processing at the time.[5] The direction in which we look is regulated by what we are thinking. For instance, over 90 per cent of right-handed people look to the left when asked to remember something and to the right when asked to mentally construct something in their imagination. For left-handed people the position is reversed.

Try it for yourself and see; ask someone how many windows there are in their house and, if they are right-handed, you will usually see their eyes move up and to the left. On the other hand, if you were to ask them what they thought a Martian would look like, they will usually look up and to the right.

The following eye movements relate to the thought processes of right-handed people; for left-handed people, everything is reversed.

The eyes move upwards to the left when we remember scenes or images. In a controlled study,[6] researchers discovered that most people move their eyes in this direction when recalling a dream, presumably because most people dream in pictures and therefore remember visual characteristics. In fact, looking up to the left can, it is thought, help you remember a dream as it triggers the brain into searching for visual images. Therefore, questions that will often result in people looking upwards to the left are: 'What is the colour of your bedroom?' or 'How many rooms are there in your house?'

The eyes move upwards to the right when we create images in our minds of things we have never seen before. Ask someone to picture a pink elephant wearing a red polka-dot tutu and, nine times out of ten, their eyes move upwards to the right.

The eyes move sideways to the left when we remember sounds, music and voices. Questions such as: 'What is your favourite song?' or 'What was the first thing someone said to you today?' will usually elicit this response.

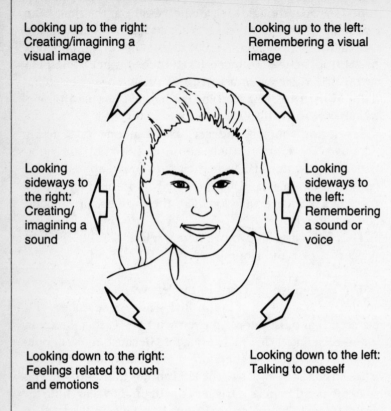

Looking up to the right:
Creating/imagining a
visual image

Looking up to the left:
Remembering a visual
image

Looking
sideways to
the right:
Creating/
imagining a
sound

Looking
sideways to
the left:
Remembering
a sound or
voice

Looking down to the right:
Feelings related to touch
and emotions

Looking down to the left:
Talking to oneself

*Figure 7.1: Eye movements and thought processes seen
in the eyes.*

When we are trying to create new sounds in our minds,
we usually look sideways and to the right. Questions that
elicit this response are: 'Imagine a seal singing the national
anthem' or 'What do you think a lobster's voice would sound
like?'

The eyes move downwards to the left when we are
talking to ourselves. If someone is looking in this direction
when you are talking to them, they will not be concentrating

on what you are saying at that moment. The position of their eyes shows that they are either evaluating what you have just said or thinking about something else.

Looking downwards to the right reveals a person is accessing feelings, whether they be smell, taste, touch or emotions. If you ask someone what it feels like to touch a stinging nettle or to describe what it feels like to be in love, he or she will usually look down and to the right.

The Benefits of Evaluating Eye Movements

Understanding eye movements can have enormous benefits. For a start, it can often help identify when someone is lying to you over a past event. If, for instance, a right-handed person looks upwards or sideways to the right when giving his version of events, the chances are he will be making it all up rather than remembering it.

Developing Communication Skills

Eye movements tell us a great deal about the way someone thinks. Once we know how a person thinks, communication becomes much easier. For instance, some children learn more easily when they read something or are shown something, whereas others need to hear it. Other children learn more effectively only when they experience it through demonstration.

This is nothing to do with intelligence, but rather with the way we process our thoughts. Often a child may appear to be a slow learner in a subject because the teacher is using a form of communication inappropriate to the child's learning ability. Change the approach to suit the child's thought patterns and the problem is often immediately solved.

It is therefore very valuable to know whether a person processes their thoughts primarily through images, sounds and words or feelings.

Generally speaking, people may be divided into three categories as far as their mental processes are concerned: visual, auditory and kinesthetic.

Visual

Visual people understand better when they see things rather than hear them. They learn and communicate more easily through pictures or images rather than just having things explained to them. They tend to see the world in pictures and, because they need to keep up with the images in their brain, they tend to speak quickly. They even use visual metaphors and phrases in their conversation, saying things like 'I see what you mean' or 'It looks okay to me.'

Auditory

Auditory people learn and communicate better when they hear things. Words are more important to them than images and their speech tends to be more controlled, measured and rhythmic. Words have more significance to them and they therefore tend to be more selective in what they say.

Auditory people usually talk using phrases such as 'It sounds good to me' or 'I hear what you're saying.'

Kinesthetic

Kinesthetic people need to feel or experience things to fully understand them. They react primarily to their feelings and often speak quite slowly. The kinesthetic person uses phrases relating to feelings such as 'I can't grasp it' or 'It feels all right.'

How to Establish whether Someone is Visual, Auditory or Kinesthetic

Of course, people very rarely fall into one category alone but there is always one which predominates. Eliciting that category is the key to developing rapport and communication skills.

You can discover how people process their thoughts by asking simple questions and observing their eye movements. For instance, if someone's eyes move predominantly upwards when discussing a subject, they would fall into the 'visual' category; if the eyes move sideways, the person would be placed in the 'auditory' category; and, finally, if the eyes move predominantly downwards to the left, the person is 'kinesthetic'.

The eye movements can be of great help to anyone whose job requires developing rapport and communication with others, whether they be teachers, sales representatives, negotiators, or even doctors and lawyers.

Improving Learning Skills

The eyes have a strong influence on our learning skills. For instance, a recent study conducted by the Medical Research Council[7] revealed that thousands of dyslexic children could be cured simply by wearing tinted spectacles. The researchers found that bright yellow, pink, green and blue tinted glasses helps children with reading difficulties. John Bald, a literacy expert and consultant to the National Curriculum Council who participated in the research, said, 'It is the most important advance in the treatment of reading difficulties I have ever seen. The family of one child I saw had spent £20,000 on special tuition and assessment before trying this tint – and the problems were solved immediately.'

The report concluded that all children with reading

difficulties should be screened as part of a regular eye examination and provided firm evidence that the eyes play a significant role in developing learning skills. Researchers are now beginning to understand that many aspects of intelligence and ability to assimilate and process information is directly influenced by our eyes, and children who were formerly considered to be 'slow learners' or 'backward' merely had problems with their eyes.

One group of researchers was so impressed by the significance of our eye movements in relation to our learning skills that they entitled their report 'Don't teach till you see the direction of their eye movements'.[8] The researchers were convinced that our eye movements reveal such vital information about our personality make-up *(see Chapter 6)*, as well as the way we process our thoughts, that knowledge of them could literally maximize a person's learning skills.

Imagine a teacher, trying to teach basic arithmetic to children. Some children will grasp it easily by seeing the sums on the blackboard, other children will understand it as they hear the teacher explain it, but others will need to experience it in a tangible form such as using money or oranges and apples as examples. Very often, some children appear to be slower and less intelligent because they are being taught in a primarily auditory style when they may be 'visual' people. Visual people often find it much more difficult to learn languages because they need more than verbal stimuli to learn well.

Closing a Sale

Likewise, a salesman will do much better in selling if he can elicit the predominant category of his prospective customer. It would be a waste of time explaining the benefits of his product or service to a visual person without showing them the benefits in black and white. A kinesthetic person, on the other hand, will need more demonstration in the sales pitch.

Effective Communication

THOUGHTS IN THE EYES

Every one of us can benefit from understanding eye movements because the quality of our lives is proportionate to the quality of our communication with ourselves and others. Many of our personal problems derive simply from poor communication. People often do not understand the meaning of what we are trying to communicate because we are communicating in a manner which they find difficult to appreciate. We simply need to learn to communicate in the most appropriate way for the person receiving the message, rather than in the manner which suits our own sensibilities.

Honesty

We have already seen that the truth of a person's statement can often be confirmed or challenged from the reaction of their pupils and the way they move their eyes in conversation. There are two other ways in which the eyes tell you whether someone is perhaps being dishonest and these relate to their willingness to look you in the eye when speaking.

The first and most obvious sign of dishonesty is when a person refuses to look you in the eye very often during a conversation. Psychologists have demonstrated that, during a normal conversation, when someone is being open and honest he will look you in the eyes between one-third and two-thirds of the time. If a person is lying or holding back information, he will look at you less than one third of the time and often turn his gaze downward toward the floor. If a person looks you in the eye for more than two-thirds of the time, it either means he finds you interesting or appealing (in which case the pupils will be dilated) or that he is hostile toward you (in which case his pupils will be contracted).

You should also be suspicious about the truth of a statement when a person rubs their eyes when talking about something. Men tend to rub their eyes vigorously whereas women use a much gentler rubbing, although this might be because they subconsciously avoid smudging make-up. This gesture, according to physiognomist, Allan Pease, is 'the brain's attempt to block out the deceit, doubt or lie or to avoid having to look at the face of a person to whom he is telling the lie'.[9]

Endnotes

1. Brophy, J., *The Human Face Reconsidered*, George G. Harrap & Co, 1962.
2. Morris, D., *Baby Watching*, Jonathon Cape, 1991.
3. Ibid, p.266.
4. Reported by Allan Pease in *Body Language*, Sheldon Press, 1981.
5. Robbins, A., *Unlimited Power*, Simon & Schuster, 1986, pp.307–31.
6. Jones, D. S. et al, 'Lateral eye-movements and dream recall', Missouri Southern State College, *Perceptual and Motor Skills* 1980 Jun Vol. 50 (3, Pt 2), p.1090.
7. Reported in the *Mail on Sunday*, 27 June 1993, p.10.
8. Day, M. E., 'Don't teach till you see the direction of their eye movements' Veterans Administration Hospital, Downey, Illinois, *Journal of Special Education* 1970, Spr Vol 4 (2), pp.233–7.
9. Reported by Allan Pease in *Body Language*, Sheldon Press, 1981, p.50.

CHAPTER 8

Love, Sex and Romance in the Eyes

The eyes can indicate affection, desire, defiance, contempt, hatred, indignation, melancholy, joy and all the emotions. They can be used to intimidate or seduce. They have a lover's language all their own ...
John Brophy, *The Human Face Reconsidered*

Love, romance and sex are all revealed in the eyes. A passionate nature, a romantic personality and even a strong sex drive can all be observed in the eyes. Psychologists and anthropologists have observed and then demonstrated in controlled studies that, in matters of love, the eyes have a language of their own.

The Eyes – Gateways of Erotic Desire

All civilizations have acknowledged the importance of the appearance of the eyes to sexual attraction. This is presumably why women from different cultures all over the world spend so much more time enhancing the appearance of their eyes than any other facial feature to make themselves more attractive. But it is only in recent years that psychologists have begun to understand the importance of the eyes in sexual attraction, romance and love.

Bronis Law Malinowski, a respected anthropologist, discovered that many tribal peoples actually considered the eyes to be the gateways of erotic desires. The eyes, he learned, are often considered paramount in sexual relations, from the initial attraction through to courtship and even love-making.

Malinowski first became intrigued with the eyes during a study of the Trobriand islanders in the Pacific. Not only did the female islanders devote a much greater amount of time and energy to decorating and elaborating their eyes than any other bodily part, but they also developed a strange and somewhat peculiar practice during love-making in which the eyes played a key role.

The practice, known as *mitakuku*, involved one partner biting the tips of their lover's eyelashes. The man would tenderly or passionately bite the tips of his lover's eyelashes during sexual foreplay and also during orgasm. Although the origins of *mitakuku* remain a mystery, it does demonstrate what ancient tribal peoples and poets have believed for thousands of years ... the eyes really do contain secrets of love. It also might explain why the islanders go through so much dental floss!

Physical Attraction and Love

Love and attraction are associated with the eyes from birth. When you were born, all you could see was the shape of your mother's face and two dots as her eyes. Even after six weeks, when your vision began to improve, what made you feel safe and what made you smile was recognizing your mother's eyes, the pupils of which were very large every time she looked at you. In fact, as a baby, you were more concerned with your mother's eyes than any of her other facial features. It wouldn't have mattered if every other facial feature was covered up, if you had been able to see no other part of your mother's face except for her eyes, you would have still instinctively known that there was a bond between you, that you were safe; and you would have smiled. As a result of your childhood, it is the eyes that remain the central stimulus for love and attraction throughout your life.

When you meet someone to whom you are physically and sexually attracted, your eyes let the person know. Fortunately their eyes also let you know whether they are attracted to you. Many people waste so much time and energy trying to find out whether another person finds them attractive, when all it takes to find out is to look closely at their eyes.

How do someone's eyes tell you whether they are attracted to you? Their pupils dilate; and the more they dilate, the more they are attracted to you. The little black hole in the middle of the eye can enlarge up to four times in size, almost totally covering the iris, when the attraction is very strong. This is a completely involuntary reaction. We do not know we are doing it and we cannot control it, but whenever we are physically attracted to another person, and whenever we have feelings of love toward a person, the one thing you can be sure of is ... our pupils dilate.

The same response happens when we are sexually excited. Researchers have shown that when sexually explicit films are shown to men, their pupils dilate to almost three times their normal size. Interestingly enough, when the same films are shown to women, their pupils dilate even more!

We are also more attracted to people who have large pupils. Subconsciously we decode the pupilliary signal. For instance, if you were to meet two identical twins of the opposite sex and one had dilated pupils but the other did not, all other things being equal, you would feel more attracted to the twin with the dilated pupils. Why? Because someone who is attracted to you is always more appealing than someone who isn't. You like the other person sometimes *because* they like you.

This is the reason why many advertisers frequently 'enhance' the appearance of models by artificially making their pupils appear dilated in their advertisements.

Photographic editors can now use sophisticated computer equipment which can make all sorts of changes to an original photograph – lengthening the legs of a model, enlarging their breasts, eliminating facial lines – but the most common change – and the most important change of all – is dilating the pupil.

The theory is of course that, by making the model appear more attractive, the product being advertised will be more appealing. The next time you look at an advert in a magazine, have a good look at the model's eyes and you will see that, in virtually every advert you come across, the pupils are significantly dilated.

Therefore whenever you want to encourage someone's interest in you, all you need do is try and ensure that your pupils are dilated when you meet. This can, as far as I know, only be achieved by one of two ways. First, you can take certain drugs (e.g. belladonna, atropine or cocaine) which will temporarily dilate the pupil, but this is not such a good idea as these drugs can be addictive and are known to cause a plethora of dangerous side effects which could permanently affect your physical and mental health. (For example, atropine affects the heart and cocaine is known to be addictive and can cause insomnia, tremors, personality changes, diarrhoea, constipation, headaches, psychosis as well as many other conditions too numerous to mention.) Interestingly enough, however, in centuries past prostitutes were known to put drops of belladonna (which contains atropin) in their eyes to make their pupils artificially dilate and thus make them more appealing to potential clients. In fact, the name 'belladonna' (literally, 'beautiful lady') got its name from this practice.

The second way to ensure that your pupils are dilated when you meet someone is completely safe, legal, and also much easier – simply arrange to meet the person in a dimly-lit room!

Dimly-lit places are a much safer way of encouraging romance. Remember, the pupils respond to light. In bright light, they contract and become small to prevent too much light entering the eyeball and damaging the retina. In dark places, the pupils dilate to allow more light to enter the eyeball so that we can see more clearly. This is why we often subconsciously choose candle-lit restaurants or dimly-lit bars on those first dates early on in a relationship – it encourages feelings of attraction! Perhaps if we had more candle-lit dinners, it might be possible to keep the excitement alive and strengthen feelings of attraction in our relationships.

Enlarged pupils – the first sign of physical attraction and sexual excitement – also trigger a response that begins the sexual relationship. According to the renowned psychologist and author, Desmond Morris, dilated pupils in two people are a signal of mutual appeal that makes both of them 'want to be more intimate, closer together, and to touch and hold one another'.[1]

How to Spot an Avowed 'Don Juan'

If you are attracted to a person but notice that in normal light conditions (i.e. not too bright or too dim) that their pupils are constricted, then despite what they may say or do, it will be very unlikely that you will be able to establish a lasting, loving relationship with them. Constricted pupils in the beginning of a relationship should ring warning bells because the eyes are, in effect, telling you that the person is not deeply attracted to you. In fact, psychology experiments have demonstrated that the only men whose pupils constrict when looking at a picture of a pretty woman who has dilated pupils are either homosexuals or what the psychologists refer to as 'Don Juan' types – girl chasers who seek to conquer a girl sexually and then move on to another, unable or unwilling to commit to a lasting relationship.

In one interesting experiment, the pupil responses of avowed 'Don Juans' were tested. These men's pupils constricted when they were shown pictures of girls with dilated pupils. Their eyes were, in effect, saying that they preferred girls who were not overtly attracted to them either because they would be less likely to become too demanding, or because they represented a greater challenge.[2]

Getting Intimate – the Lover's Gaze

After the pupils have dilated, the next intimate signal is also in the eyes, but this time it lies in the way we look at the object of our desires. Experiments into gazing have revealed that there is a lover's gaze; a mutual gaze which is stronger and more intense than seen in ordinary social situations or between strangers. One study published in the *Journal of Psychology*[3] looked specifically at the way we gaze in relation to the degree of love felt. The researchers demonstrated that the way in which lovers gazed at each other varied according to the way they felt about each other. If the bond between lovers was strong, the gaze was longer and more intense than the gaze between two less committed lovers.

Getting Sexual

Psychologists have demonstrated that when we socialize, our gaze is usually limited to a triangle made up of the eyes and mouth. However, the same experiments have demonstrated that when we are sexually interested in a person, our gaze moves from the other peron's eyes, below their mouth to their chest or breasts and even down to their crotch. This is another subconscious response which informs the other person that you are sexually interested, and if they are interested in you, they will return the gaze.

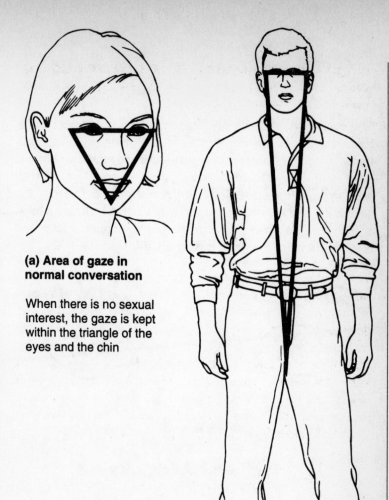

(a) Area of gaze in normal conversation

When there is no sexual interest, the gaze is kept within the triangle of the eyes and the chin

(b) Area of gaze when sexual interest

When there is sexual interest, the area of the gaze extends from the eyes to the genitals

Figure 8.1a: Area of gaze in normal conversation.
Figure 8.1b: Area of gaze with sexual interest.

129

Eyebrows – Passion, Sex Drive and Lasting Relationships

The eyebrows, according to masters of Siang Mien, reveal a lot about a person's characteristics in loving relationships. For instance, people with very thin eyebrows shaped like a new moon are said to be very passionate and emotional with strong sex drives. *(See Chapter 6, Figure 6.3f.)*

Thick, curly eyebrows, on the other hand, indicate a lack of affection and it is said that people with such eyebrows find it difficult to maintain lasting relationships.

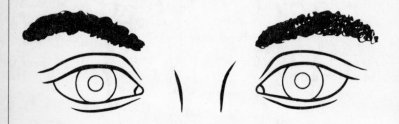

Figure 8.2: Curly eyebrows indicating a lack of affection.

Eyelids and Frigidity

Single eyelids, as in Figure 8.3, are said to represent a cold-hearted, sometimes frigid personality and are consequently associated with people who have difficulty forming lasting relationships.

Libido

Siang Mien masters also considered that a strong sex drive was associated with people in whom the whites of the eyes were slightly reddish in colour. Unlike redness seen as raised

Figure 8.3: Single eyelid.

blood vessels, which can be caused by high blood pressure and a high-fat diet as well as allergies and infection or irritation to the membrane surrounding the eye, the Siang Mien masters were referring to the redness caused by clusters of small red dots.

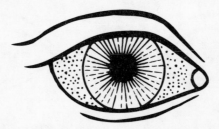

Figure 8.4: Clusters of red dots on the sclera – strong sex drive.

Relationships

In the science of Siang Mien, the area under the eyes is known as the love region. It is the one area of the face that is considered to reveal most about our relationships. According to Lailan Young, an expert in Siang Mien, if the area is pinkish or luminous all is well and the relationship is going smoothly. If there are lines under the eyes as in Figure 8.5 it is said to indicate a broken heart or a serious disappointment in friendship or family relationships.

131

Figure 8.5: Lines under the eyes.

An indentation at the outer area of the lower eyelids as in Figure 8.6 is considered a characteristic of a person who will be faithful and loyal to his marriage partner. To such a person, marriage is taken seriously and considered a lifetime commitment.

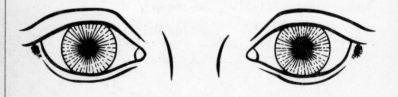

Figure 8.6: Indentations at the outer edge of the eyelid.

Choosing the Right Partner

Choosing the right partner can be difficult at the best of times. How can we be sure a person is truly compatible and that a relationship will last? Well, who knows! People resort to astrology, palmistry, graphology, and even computerized psychoanalysis to try and find out if a particular person is right for them. I always feel we are best guided by our intuition and, as one wise old lady once advised me, if in doubt, do nowt! However, for those people who do not trust their intuition, the eyes offer a fascinating, alternative method to help determine the suitability of two people.

The first thing to look at is, as mentioned above, a person's pupils. If the pupils are not dilated in the initial stages of a relationship, regardless of what the person may say or do, the likelihood that they are really attracted to you is very slim indeed. If the pupils are noticeably constricted, it is extremely doubtful that they are emotionally able to form a lasting relationship. More often than not, a person whose pupils are constricted is probably only after a sexual conquest.

The pupils reveal physical attraction, but lasting relationships require mental and emotional compatibility. It is generally accepted, for instance, that there must be a balancing of two opposites to create harmony. We see this balancing of opposites throughout Nature – cold and hot, dark and light, wet and dry, strong and weak – but the same applies to human relationships. Two partners need to complement each other, balancing one's weaknesses with the other's strengths. If you are not sure whether you or your partner are well suited emotionally or mentally, take a good look at each other's eyes.

It is well known that extroverts complement introverts, and by the same token, right-brained people complement left-brained people. According to the Rayid interpretation of eyes, a person with a 'jewel' iris is suited to a person with 'flower' irises, whereas a person with a 'stream' iris is more drawn to a person with 'shaker' irises for long-term relationships.

Pregnancy and Childbirth

Whilst there are no markings in the eyes, as far as I know, which reveal whether or not a woman is pregnant, the North American Indians discovered an interesting way of determining whether a pregnant woman was going to have a boy or a girl.

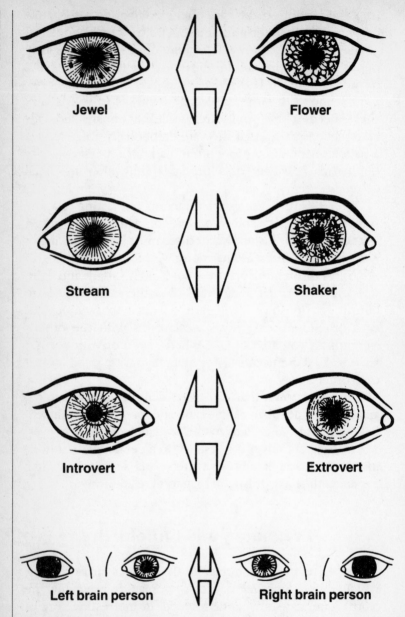

Jewel

Flower

Stream

Shaker

Introvert

Extrovert

Left brain person

Right brain person

Figure 8.7: Choosing the right partner for your personality.

The North American Indian technique is very simple. They look for fish-hook shaped blood vessels in the whites of the pregnant woman's eyes, immediately outside the iris at the position of 5 o'clock and 7 o'clock as in Figure 8.8. If the fish-hook blood vessels appear in the *right* eye, the woman can expect a girl and if the vessels are in the *left* eye, she can expect a boy. If there is a fish-hook blood vessel in *both* eyes, then twins may be expected, although it may just mean that the woman has had other children. On those rare occasions when twins are not expected and a woman has not had any children before, the right eye takes precedence and therefore indicates that the baby is a girl.[4]

This may seem, at first, to be rather bizarre . . . until you connect it with the iridology chart in Chapter 2. The position of 5 o'clock and 7 o'clock in the iris records the condition of the ovary, uterus and vagina! It is also interesting to note that, in the Rayid system of iris analysis, the left brain (and thus the right eye) is related to female relationships and the right brain (and thus the left eye) is related to male relationships.

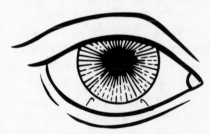

Figure 8.8: Fish-hook blood vessels in the sclera at 5 o'clock and 7 o'clock indicating the sex of a pregnant woman's child.

At about the time I discovered this method of determining the sex of an unborn baby, my wife and I were expecting our first child. I had a look at my wife's eyes to see if I could find any fish-hook blood vessels and, lo and behold, there were distinct fish-hook blood vessels in her right eye. We took it all with no more than a pinch of salt but we did indeed have a little girl. And, whilst I have not done any serious research, the marking did, in fact, work for the other pregnant women with whom we had antenatal classes, and it has also been correct for the few pregnant women who have participated in my seminars.

Making Relationships Work
and Saving Marriages

Not only do all relationships begin with the eyes, but they can also be successfully maintained with an understanding of each other's needs as gleaned from the eyes. Many of our personal problems derive simply from poor communication. In fact, when I worked in matrimonial law, one of the first things I noticed, which has since been borne out by the findings of clinical psychologists, was that many marriages often break down because the partners simply are not able to communicate with each other.

In the beginning of most relationships, both partners will usually communicate their feelings in every way possible. They will buy each other gifts, tell each other how wonderful they are, and embrace whenever and wherever possible. But as the relationship progresses things change and each partner will tend to communicate his or her feelings in ways which are more personally appropriate. These ways may not, however, be appropriate to the other partner.

Often, for example, a husband loves his wife but simply cannot communicate that love in a way that is acceptable to her. A visual person who is told 'I love you' thinks 'talk is cheap'; he or she needs to be shown that love through cards, flowers and gifts. An auditory person who is continually being hugged by a kinesthetic partner says, 'Stop treating me like a slab of meat.' Such a person needs to be told how much they are loved. Whereas a kinesthetic person is unimpressed by expensive gifts, they need to be caressed and hugged in order to feel loved.

Finding the best way to say "I love you"

There are many ways to say "I love you" – some people say it with gifts (eg. flowers or jewellery), some say it with hugs and kisses and others just say it. The question is: "Which is the best way to say it to your partner?

The Visual Personality

- Tends to favour looking upwards when looking away during a conversation

  or

- Uses expressions such as "I see", "look here" and "in my view".
- Needs to be shown an expression of love and therefore responds best to gifts or cards

The Auditory Personality

- Tends to favour looking sideways when looking away during a conversation

  or

- Uses expressions such as "I hear", "listen here" and "sounds good!".
- Needs to hear you say "I love you" and romantic whisperings in order to *feel* loved

The Kinesthetic Personality

  or

- Tends to favour looking down when looking away during a conversation
- Uses expressions such as "I feel", "feels good" and "it strikes me".
- Needs physical affection (eg. hugs, kisses, holding hands) in order to *feel* loved

Figure 8.9: Finding the best way to say 'I love you'.

137

We simply need to learn to communicate with our partner in the most appropriate way to make our relationships work. This can be established through the direction in which they move their eyes *(see Chapter 6)* and also by their eye colouring. Jewel eyes are generally auditory people, those with flower irises are visual people and stream eyes are seen in kinesthetic people.

The ability to understand one another and communicate effectively is perhaps the greatest of all the secrets in the eyes.

Endnotes

1. Morris, D., *The Pocket Guide to Manwatching*, p.264, Triad Grafton Books, 1982.
2. Ibid, p.264.
3. Goldstein, M.A., Kilroy, C. M., Van de Voort, D., 'Gaze as a function of conversation and degree of love', Illinois State University, *Journal of Psychology* Mar 1976 Vol. 92 (2), pp.227–34.
4. Maxwell, J., *The Eye-Body Connection*, p.107, Warner Books, 1980.

CHAPTER 9

At-A-Glance:
A Quick Guide to Personal Analysis through the Eyes

It is now known that the eyes truly are a mirror of our physical and emotional health. Acting as the body's Yellow Pages, they function as an accurate index of what is occurring within the body and mind.
Dr Jacob Liberman OD, PhD

This At-A-Glance guide is designed as an easy-to-use reference to help you quickly analyse a person by looking at their eyes. Listed below are descriptions and illustrations of the common signs and features in and around the eyes, together with brief explanations of their meanings. Fuller explanations have been given in the preceding chapters.

The shape of the eye

The Dragon

Strong personality, brave and courageous. Creative, social and often generous

The Cow

Trustworthy, open, honest and direct

The Peacock
Emotional person, driven by feelings

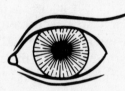

The Tiger

Persistent, rational and forward thinking
The Fox
Cunning nature, also noted for meanness

The Triangle and the Chicken

Authoritarian and manipulative

The New Moon

Tendency to dishonesty and cunning

General features of the eye

Small eyes
Reserved, cautious and secretive
Large eyes
Open, impulsive and passionate

Pointed inner tips

Difficulties with concentration
Indentations at the outer edges

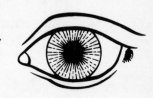

Faithful and loyal
Bulging, protruding eyes

If continuously bulging – thyroid problems
If only temporarily bulging – fear

Eyes close together

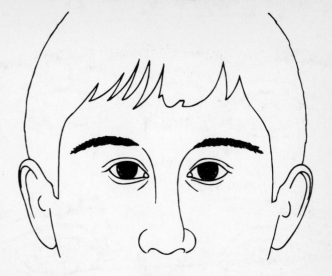

Reserved, shy
Deep-set eyes

Withdrawn, secretive

Eyebrows

Ideal

Power and authority

Broom

Up-good at initiating a project but not at finishing it

Down – lacks drive to initiate a project but good in the final stages

Hero's

Energetic, ambitious and organized

Chaotic

Usually found on people who have good physiques but scattered thoughts and poor concentration

Triangle

Capable of courage, decisive but often selfish. If the ends are noticeably pointed, it indicates that the person is clever, decisive, but with a capacity to be cruel.

New moon

Emotional, passionate, if thick – prone to bouts of hysteria.

Eyebrows close to the eyes

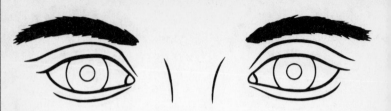

Good decision maker, impatient with a tendency to fidget

One eyebrow higher than the other

Susceptible to mood changes – emotional highs and lows

Vertical hairs on the inner part of the eyebrow

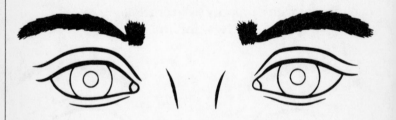

Difficulty in relationships with immediate family

Short eyebrows

Short tempered, selfish and often impatient
Curly eyebrows

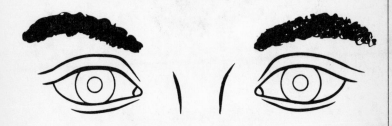

Cold-hearted, lack of affection

Eyelashes

Curled up

Optimistic or passionate

Thick and long

Emotional

Fine

Cool and detached

Eyelids

Puffy or darkened lower lid

Kidney problems

Puffy upper lid

Gall Bladder problems

Yellow patches on the eyelids

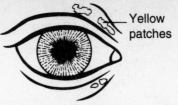
Yellow
patches

Problems with cholesterol metabolism
Lines in the lower eyelid

Serious disappointments in past relationships
Pale colouring on the inside of the eyelid

The inside of the eyelid should appear a pink, fleshy colour. If it is pale/white it indicates anaemia.

Anaemia
Veraguth fold in the upper eyelid

Severe, chronic depression

Fluttering of the eyelid
Depression, anxiety or fatigue
Eyelids closed for prolonged periods
Boredom or fatigue

Iris

Blue

Hereditary tendency to acid health complaints (e.g. arthritis, rheumatism, ulcers, asthma and skin complaints). Delicate skin needs protection from UV rays.

In a child – tendency to display inhibited nature.

Brown

Hereditary tendency to problems related to fat metabolism and digestion. Skin better able to produce pigment to protect against UV rays.

In a child – tendency to be less inhibited than blue-eyed children.

Tight, straight fibres

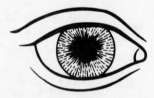

Strong physical constitution. Recuperates fast from illness, but has a weak nervous system. Often unable to relax, needs to be constantly doing things.

Loosely connected fibres

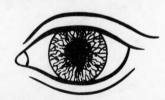

Weak physical constitution. Needs to take greater care of

physical health but is better able to relax and cope with mental stress.

White-yellow arc on upper and/or lower part of iris

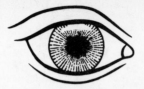

Initial stages of hardening of the arteries due to excess cholesterol and/or inorganic mineral deposits.

White-yellow ring around the periphery of the iris

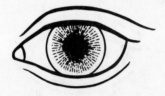

Advanced stages of hardening of the arteries due to excess cholesterol and/or inorganic mineral deposits.

Dark rim on the outer edge of the iris

Poor circulation, underfunctioning skin with tendency to cold extremities and minor skin complaints.

Nerve wreath close to the pupil

Tension in colon; associated with constipation. Also

introverted personality with difficulty in 'letting go' of past hurts/memories.

Nerve wreath far away from the pupil

Weak intestines; associated with sluggish bowel movements. Also extroverted personality.

Jagged-edged nerve wreath

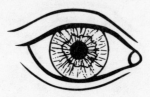

Spastic colon; tendency to Irritable Bowel Syndrome

White halo around the pupil

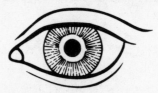

Hyperacidity in the stomach and intestines with tendency to indigestion and stomach ulcers.

Copper coloured arc in the upper section of the iris

Wilson's disease – poor metabolism of copper

String of pearls around the periphery of the iris

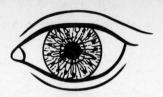

Congested lymphatic system with tendency to allergies, hay fever, oedema and infections.

Hole in the iris fibres at 6 o'clock

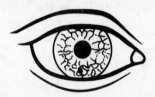

Tendency to varicose veins

Discolourations in the iris

White = inflammation, acidity, hyperactivity

Yellow = congestion

Orange and brown = toxicity (NB Toxicity will appear as a darker brown in a brown iris)

Black = degeneration

Circular rings in the iris

Accumulated tension

The pupil

Discoloured grey

Cataract

Discoloured green
Glaucoma
Unequal-sized pupils

Imbalanced nervous system; possible stroke
Small pupils

If continuous – indicates current stress or pain
If temporary – indicates a strong dislike, revulsion or physical pain
NB The pupils will naturally contract in bright light

Non-reactive pin-hole pupils
Serious health problems, suspected drug abuse, possibly syphilis.

Dilated pupils

If continuous – indicates nervous exhaustion or suspected drug abuse
If temporary – indicates excitement or physical attraction

The whites of the eyes (the sclera)

Yellow patches

Pingueculae: may be caused by prolonged exposure to sun or wind; considered an early warning sign for problems with cholesterol metabolism.

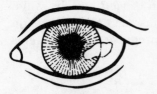

Pterygium: may be caused by prolonged exposure to sun or wind; considered an early warning sign for problems with cholesterol metabolism.

Blood vessels

Varicose veins

Kidney problems

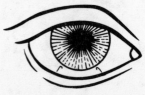

In the eyes of a pregnant woman to determine the sex of a baby. Fish-hook blood vessels in the *right* eye at 5 o'clock and 7 o'clock indicate the woman is having a girl, whereas if they are found in the *left* eye she will be expecting a boy. NB If a woman has been pregnant before, the blood vessels from the earlier pregnancy may still remain.

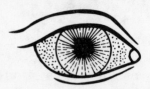

Cluster of red dots – high sex drive

Prolific red blood vessels – high blood pressure, eye infection/irritation or kidney problems

Red tint
 liver problems
Yellow tint
 jaundice
Blue tint
 brittle bone disease (Osteogenesis imperfecta)
 Two sides of the sclera around the iris are showing

normal
Three sides of the sclera around the iris showing

White showing above the iris: hypersensitive, self-centred, can be brutish

White showing below the iris: oversensitive, self-conscious

Four sides of the sclera around the iris showing

If continuous – bright, decisive and efficient. Good at managing other people.

If temporary – may be caused by fear.

Eye movements

Rapid movements of the eyeball

Psychologically disturbed (e.g. post-traumatic stress disorder, schizophrenia, phobias and personality disorders)

Eye contact during conversation

Good – indicates good self-esteem, intelligence and honesty.

Poor – indicates poor self-esteem, lack of intelligence, depression or dishonesty.

More than 70 per cent of the time – shows strong interest (especially when coupled with dilated pupils showing a strong like or attraction)

Less than 30 per cent of the time – shows lack of interest

Eye movements during conversation
More often to the left – assertive, shrewd and suspicious nature

More often to the right – emotional and sensitive

Eye movements in response to specific questions

Looking up to the right: Creating/imagining a visual image

Looking up to the left: Remembering a visual image

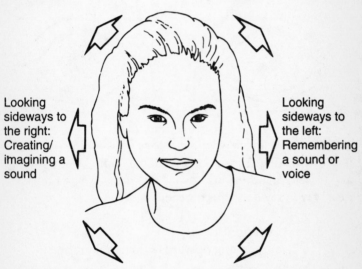

Looking sideways to the right: Creating/imagining a sound

Looking sideways to the left: Remembering a sound or voice

Looking down to the right: Feelings related to touch and emotions

Looking down to the left: Talking to oneself

Narrowing the eyes

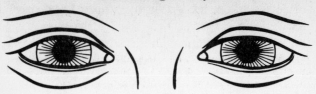

Anger, disgust
Widening the eyes

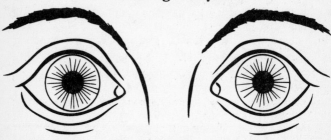

Fear, excitement

There are many ways to say 'I love you' – some people say
it with gifts (e.g. flowers or jewellery), some say it with hugs
and kisses and others just say it. The question is: which is the
best way to say it to your partner?

The Visual Personality

Tends to favour looking upwards when looking away
during a conversation.

Uses expressions such as 'I see', 'look here' and 'in my
view'.

Needs to be shown an expression of love and therefore
responds best to gifts or cards.

The Auditory Personality

Tends to favour looking sideways when looking away
during a conversation.

Uses expression such as 'I hear', 'listen here' and 'sounds
good'.

Needs to hear you say 'I love you' and other romantic

Finding the best way to say "I love you"

There are many ways to say "I love you" – some people say it with gifts (eg. flowers or jewellery), some say it with hugs and kisses and others just say it. The question is: "Which is the best way to say it to your partner?

The Visual Personality

- Tends to favour looking upwards when looking away during a conversation

  or

- Uses expressions such as "I see", "look here" and "in my view".
- Needs to be shown an expression of love and therefore responds best to gifts or cards

The Auditory Personality

- Tends to favour looking sideways when looking away during a conversation

  or

- Uses expressions such as "I hear", "listen here" and "sounds good!".
- Needs to hear you say "I love you" and romantic whisperings in order to *feel* loved

The Kinesthetic Personality

  or

- Tends to favour looking down when looking away during a conversation
- Uses expressions such as "I feel", "feels good" and "it strikes me".
- Needs physical affection (eg. hugs, kisses, holding hands) in order to *feel* loved

Figure 8.9: Finding the best way to say 'I love you'.

161

whisperings in order to *feel* loved.

The Kinesthetic Personality

Tends to favour looking down when looking away during a conversation.

Uses expressions such as 'I feel', 'feels good' or 'it strikes me'.

Needs physical affection (e.g. hugs, kisses, holding hands) in order to *feel* loved.

Bibliography

Axtell, Roger E., *Gestures: The do's and taboos of body language around the world*, John Wiley & Sons Inc., 1991

Benjamin, Harry, *Better Sight Without Glasses*, Health for All Publishing Co, 1929

Bishop, S.W.E., *The Secret of Eye-Signs*, S & D Bishop Ltd, 1988

Brophy, John, *The Human Face Reconsidered*, George G. Harrap & Co, 1962

Hall, Dorothy, *Iridology*, Angus & Robertson, 1980

Hess, E., *The Tell-Tale Eye*, Van Nostrand Reinhold, NY, 1975

Jackson, Adam J., *Iridology: A guide to iris analysis and preventive health care*, Optima, Little, Brown, 1992

Jensen, Dr Bernard, *The Science and Practice of Iridology*, B. Jensen, 1952

Johnson, Denny, *What the Eye Reveals: An introduction to the Rayid method of iris interpretation*, Rayid Publications, 1984

Landau, Terry, *About Faces: The evolution of the human face*, Bantam Doubleday, 1989

Liberman, Jacob, *Light: Medicine of the future*, Bear & Co, 1991

Liggett, John, *The Human Face*, Constable & Co, 1974

Lowen, MD, Alexander, *The Language of the Body*, Collier Macmillan Publishers, 1958

Maxwell, Jessica, *The Eye–Body Connection*, Warner Books, 1980

Morris, Desmond, *The Pocket Guide to Manwatching*, Triad Grafton, 1982

—, *Baby Watching*, Jonathon Cape, 1991

Pease, Allan, *Body Language*, Sheldon Press, 1981

Robbins, Anthony, *Unlimited Power*, Simon & Schuster, 1986

Soo, Professor Chee, *The Chinese Art of Chiang Ming*, Gordon & Cremonesi, 1979

Young, Lailan, *Secrets of the Face*, Coronet, 1984

Youngson, Dr Robert, *Everything You Need to Know About Eyes*, Clio Press Ltd, 1990

Useful Addresses

Iridology

Canada

Iridologists'Association of Canada
5150 Dundas St W
Suite 201
Etobicoke
Ontario

The Canadian Institute of Iridology
2500 Bathurst St
Suite 201
Toronto
Ontario M6B 2Y8

Germany

Institute für Irisdiagnostik und Ganzheitstherapie
Pastor Felke Institut
Postfach 100
D-7258 Heimsheim

United Kingdom

UK College of Iris Analysis
12 Upper Station Rd
Radlett
Herts WD7 8BX

International Association of Clinical Iridologists
853 Finchley Rd
London NW11 8LX

United States

National Iridology Research Association
PO Box 33637
Seattle, WA 98133

Bernard Jensen International
24360 Old Wagon Rd
Escondido, CA 92027

Rayid System of Iridology

Rayid Publications
PO Box 1839
Goleta, CA 93116

The Bates Method

Australia

Janet Goodrich
Natural Vision Improvement
Cabooltre
PO Box QU 4510

United Kingdom

The Bates Association of Great Britain
Friars Court
11 Tarmount Lane
Shoreham-by-Sea
West Sussex
BN43 6RQ

United States

Vision Training Institute
11030 Meadow View Rd
El Cajon, CA 92020

Meir Schneider Centre for Self Healing
1718 Tarawal St
Southern California, CA 94116

Eye Movement Desensitization and Reprocessing (EMDR) Technique

France

Francois Bonnell MD
Chindes Ribas
La Romarine
St Marc
Jaumejarde
13100 Aix-en-Provence

Germany

Arne Hofmann MD
Friedel Anderstrasse 2
D-61440
Oberusel

Israel

Elan Shapiro
PO Box 187
Ramat Yishay
30095

Netherlands

A De Jongh
Psychologist
ACTA
Dept of Social Dentistry/Dental Health Education
Louweswegg 1
1066 EA
Amsterdam

Norway

Atle Dyregrov Phd
Centre for Crisis Psychology
Fabrikkgt 5
N 5037
Solheimsviken

United Kingdom

Mr John Spector MSc, CPsychol, AFBPsF
Consultant Psychologist
Shrodells Unit
Watford General Hospital
Vicarage Rd
Watford
Herts
WD1 8HB

United States

EMDR Institute Inc.
PO Box 51010
Pacific Grove, CA 93950–6010

Neuro-Linguistic Programming (NLP)

Canada

NLP Canada Training and Consulting Inc
400 Walmer Rd
Suite 1808
Toronto
Ontario M5P 2X7

United Kingdom

Pace Personal Development
86 South Hill Park
London NW3 2SN

London Personal Development Centre
2 Thayer St
London W1M 5LG

United States

Robbins Research Institute
1223 Camino Del Mar
Del Mar, CA 92014

Miscellaneous

United States

Jacob Liberman, OD, PhD
PO Box 4058
Aspen, Colorado 81612

Ronald Waldorf
EyeDynamics Inc
2291 205th St
Suite 203
Torrance, CA 90501

Index

Page numbers in italic type refer to illustrations.